A Complete Guide to the
Engine Houses of
West Cornwall

Damian Nance
and
Kenneth Brown

Dedicated to Dicon Nance
Cornish mining enthusiast, model maker, mentor and father

Lightmoor Press

Pumping engine houses of Wheal Trewavas, near Porthleven, before their consolidation. The more distant house was erected on Old Engine shaft in 1834, whereas the nearer of the two was built to house a 45-inch Harvey and Co. engine erected on New Engine (or Rogers') shaft in 1838. Both have separate stacks built higher on the cliff, the nearer one constructed entirely in stonework (2000).

Front cover (main picture) The spectacularly positioned engine houses of the Crowns section of Botallack Mine – the 30-inch pumping engine on Crowns Engine shaft (centre) and Pearce's all-enclosed 24-inch winding engine (2009).

Contents

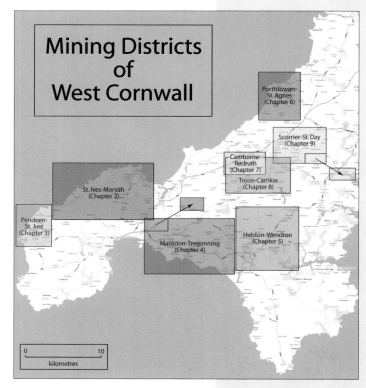

Acknowledgements

The information for the descriptions given herein comes from many sources and many people, and we are indebted to all. RDN has also benefitted from conversations with Gerald Williams, Kingsley Rickard, Phil Hosken and other members of the Trevithick Society, and has enjoyed the company and hospitality of Clive Barton, Jessamine Kendall, Matthew Lanyon, Richard and Brigid Legge, Christopher Nance, Jonny and Els Nance, Paul Otto, Toby Procter and Graham Tucker while taking photographs in Cornwall, and the love and support of Caroline Temple throughout the book's preparation. A grant from the Ohio University Research Council to RDN funded a significant portion of the field research necessary to complete this book and is gratefully acknowledged.

Photography throughout by Damian Nance, unless otherwise credited.

Published by Lightmoor Press

© Lightmoor Press, Damian Nance and Kenneth Brown 2014

British Library Cataloguing-in-Publication Data. A catalogue record for this book is available from the British Library

ISBN 13: 9781899889 85 3

Lightmoor Press
Unit 144b, Lydney Trading Estate, Harbour Road, Lydney, Gloucestershire GL15 5EJ
www.lightmoor.co.uk

Lightmoor Press is an imprint of Black Dwarf Lightmoor Publications Ltd

Designed by Alan Kittridge

The cylinder top (foreground), valve bonnets (behind), piston rod and parallel motion (above) of the all-enclosed 27-inch winding engine at Levant Mine near Pendeen. Built by Harvey and Co. of Hayle to the design of Francis Mitchell in 1840, the engine ran continuously until the mine closed in 1930 and is the oldest surviving beam engine in Cornwall. It was restored to working condition in 1992 by members of the Trevithick Society and is now regularly operated under steam by the National Trust (1990).

CHAPTER 1 **Introduction**

In no area of the world has metalliferous mining been of greater importance or longevity than it has in Cornwall, and it is in recognition of this extraordinary heritage and the global influence of the pioneering technology developed here that the county's mining landscape was named a UNESCO World Heritage Site in 2006, on a par with the Pyramids of Giza and the Great Wall of China. The importance of Cornwall's mineral wealth has been known since the time of the Ancient Greeks who traded with the Cassiterides ("tin islands") as early as the 5th century BC. During the Middle Ages, the industry was considered to be of such importance that its miners were granted special privileges and placed under the separate legal jurisdiction of the stannary ("tin mining") courts. However, it was not until the Industrial Revolution of the 18th and 19th centuries that the full measure of this remarkable resource was exploited. During peak production in the mid-19th century, Cornwall and neighbouring South Devon produced almost half of the world's supply of copper (reaching a peak output of over 13,000 tons in 1856) and over half of the world's supply of tin (with a peak output of almost 11,000 tons in 1871). Although these two metals dominated its output, the county also produced substantial quantities of lead, silver, arsenic and tungsten as well as significant amounts of zinc, iron, uranium, nickel, cobalt, manganese and bismuth. Only at the end of the 20th century, when the cost of working ever deeper deposits fell victim to cheaper foreign production, did this long and celebrated history of mining activity come to an end.

What made the unparalleled productivity of the 19th century possible was the harbinger of the Industrial Revolution itself, namely the invention of a reciprocating steam engine, or beam engine, capable of driving pumps that could keep the ever-deepening mines free of water. Invented by Thomas Newcomen early in the 18th century and greatly improved by James Watt in the second half of that century, the beam engine was brought to the peak of its development (as the Cornish engine) early in the 19th century by the Cornishman Richard Trevithick. Reciprocation was effected by placing a rocking beam between the piston, which moved up and down in a vertical cylinder, and the pumps in the shaft, which were worked by the up-and-down movement of the beam. Modified for rotary motion with the addition of a crank and flywheel, the beam engine was later adapted both for hoisting and for driving ore crushing machinery. Although smaller beam engines were commonly built as self-contained units that could be dismantled and moved, those used most widely in Cornwall were of the "house-

The Camborne-Redruth mining district in decline in about 1905 looking ENE from Dolcoath Mine towards Carn Brea hill (right). At least 20 chimney stacks and 10 engine houses are visible, including those of Dolcoath old stamps (foreground left), Old Cook's Kitchen Mine (upper right), New Cook's Kitchen Mine (upper left), Dolcoath California stamps (middle left) and from left to right in the distance, East Pool, North Tincroft, Carn Brea and South Tincroft mines.

Cutaway of a typical Cornish pumping engine showing how reciprocating movement between the upright steam cylinder (indoors) and the pump rod (outdoors) was effected by a massive rocking beam pivoted on the front (bob) wall of the engine house (drawing by Max Millar).

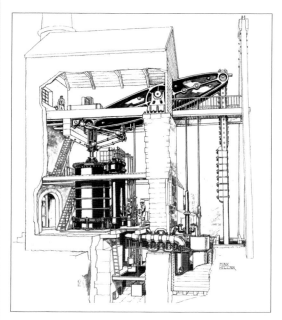

built" variety. That is, they were permanently built into engine houses with the beam pivoted on an especially strengthened end wall. The working parts of the engine were thereby enclosed within the house while the working end of the beam remained outside. Because they were heavily built to withstand the operational stresses of these massive beam engines, many engine houses have survived the century or more of neglect since the engines they contained were removed, and today stand as silent monuments to the mining industry for which the region was once justly famous. Indeed, nothing has come to symbolize the county's rich mining heritage more than the castle-like engine houses that form such prominent and characteristic features of the Cornish landscape.

This book aims to provide an illustrated guide to the surviving engine houses of West Cornwall using contemporary and older photographs supplemented with brief descriptions. The descriptions of the engine houses outline the histories of the mines they represent, summarize what is known of the engines they once contained, and provide simple interpretations of some of their key features. Like all guides, the book is not meant solely for the enthusiast, nor is it an exhaustive treatment. Instead, it is an overview intended for all those interested in these remarkable structures.

Geology

The metalliferous mining province of southwest England, which is known worldwide for the wealth and variety of its mineral deposits, owes its origin to the emplacement, some 300 million years ago, of a suite of granite bodies that collectively constitute the Cornubian batholith. Intruded into the deformed sedimentary rocks of Cornwall and Devon along what is now the spine of the Cornubian peninsula, the granites and the deformation of their host rocks are manifestations of the *Variscan orogeny*, a mountain-building episode caused by a collision between the continents of southern Europe and Africa at the end of the Paleozoic Era.

The host rocks into which these granites were intruded are predominantly shales and sandstones that were deposited some 330 to 410 million years ago during the Devonian and Carboniferous periods. Known locally as **killas**, these sedimentary rocks generally record marine deposition in a subsiding oceanic trough between the encroaching continental landmasses and are often associated with contemporary volcanic rocks and basaltic intrusions known locally as **greenstones**. In South Devon, the coeval deposition of limestone marks local areas of clearer, shallower seas.

As collision ensued, ocean-floor rocks trapped between the colliding continents were thrust upwards onto the host rocks to form the well-known serpentine stone of the Lizard Complex on Cornwall's southern-most peninsula. At the same time, the host sedimentary and volcanic rocks were deformed into a series of major folds and faults with broadly east-west orientations. The accompanying heat and pressure converted the finer grained sedimentary rocks into poor quality slate, the grain of which is generally aligned ENE.

Emplacement of the Cornubian batholith generally followed the deformation and alteration of the host rocks, and occurred as a consequence of the melting of continental crust that had become thickened as a result of the collision. Intrusion of individual granite bodies baked the surrounding host rocks to produce broad border zones or **aureoles** that are characterized by speckled rocks known as **spotted slates**. Finally, on consolidation and cooling of the granites, sheets of granitic magma were intruded into fissures in the host rocks to form tabular bodies called *porphyry dykes* that comprise a finer grained granitic rock known locally as **elvan**.

Ore Minerals

The great variety of economic **(ore)** and non-economic **(gangue)** minerals that have long made Cornwall and neighbouring South Devon a haven for mineralogists and collectors owes its origin to a complex sequence of mineralization during cooling and

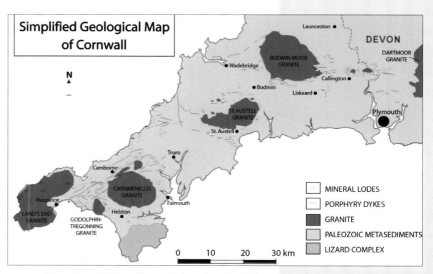

consolidation of the Cornubian batholith. The primary phase of economic (tin-tungsten-copper) mineralization is attributed to the evolution of hot, aqueous (*hydrothermal*) fluids during final solidification of the granite bodies.

Townroath Vugga – an adit, or drainage tunnel, carved both naturally and by miners into Townroath lode at Wheal Coates near St. Agnes. The partially excavated lode flanks an inclined dyke of pinkish elvan. The 36-inch pumping engine at Townroath shaft (served by the adit) sits at the cliff top.

Simplified map of the geology of Cornwall showing the main granite bodies (in red) that make up the Cornubian batholith, the sedimentary and volcanic rocks (in green) into which the granites were intruded, some of the main granitic sheets or dykes (pink lines), and the generally ENE to east-west pattern of mineralized faults or lodes (black lines). The ocean floor rocks of the Lizard peninsula are shown in purple.

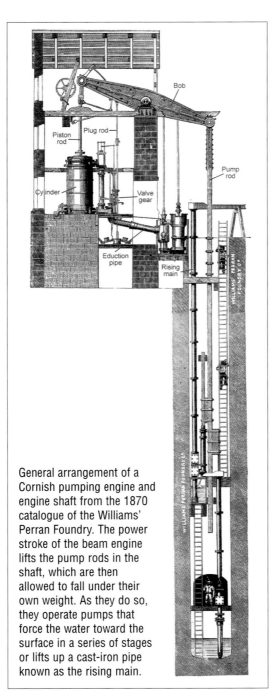

General arrangement of a Cornish pumping engine and engine shaft from the 1870 catalogue of the Williams' Perran Foundry. The power stroke of the beam engine lifts the pump rods in the shaft, which are then allowed to fall under their own weight. As they do so, they operate pumps that force the water toward the surface in a series of stages or lifts up a cast-iron pipe known as the rising main.

Driven by convection, these redistributed and precipitated minerals into networks of fractures that had developed in the cooling granites and their adjacent host rocks. Hence, a crude temperature zonation may develop in which the higher temperature (*hypothermal*) minerals occur closer to the granite bodies than those deposited in medium- (*mesothermal*) and low-temperature (*epithermal*) veins.

Principal among the mineralized fractures are the mineralized faults or **lodes**. These vein systems usually run parallel to the east-west to ENE-trending grain of the host rock (*normal lodes*), but may also cut across this grain either at a slight angle (*caunter lodes*) or at roughly right angles (*cross-courses*). In general, the earlier hypothermal minerals, such as tin and copper, occur in normal lodes, whereas later mesothermal and epithermal veins containing lead, zinc and iron minerals occupy N-S cross-courses. Other forms of mineralization include *stockwork* deposits of interlacing mineralized veinlets, and *stratiform* and *replacement* deposits formed by the wholesale alteration of granite or host rock by permeating mineralized fluids.

In Cornwall, the ores exploited came in many mineral forms but typically made up only a few percent of the lode. As a result, a significant amount of crushing and processing was needed to convert the mined ore to a saleable product. The principal ore of tin was the oxide *cassiterite* (SnO_2), the final processed form of which was called **black tin**. Copper ore came in a variety of mineral forms, including the sulphides *chalcopyrite* ($CuFeS$), *chalcocite* (Cu_2S) and *bornite* (Cu_5FeS_4), the oxide *cuprite* (Cu_2O) and the blue and green carbonates *azurite* and *malachite*. Other important ores included the lead and zinc sulphides *galena* (PbS) and *sphalerite* (ZnS), the iron oxides *hematite* (Fe_2O_3) and *magnetite* (Fe_3O_4), and the tungsten ore *wolframite*. In some areas, galena was also an important source of silver. Arsenic, which was an important byproduct of the mining industry, was produced largely from the iron sulphide *arsenopyrites* (FeAsS).

Conversion of the processed copper and tin ores to metals required further extractive processing known as **smelting**. In the 18th century, copper smelting was carried out at several locations in Cornwall, most notably at Copperhouse in Hayle, but rather than importing the necessary coal, it soon became more economical to ship the ore to smelters around Swansea, close to the coalfields of South Wales. Tin smelting, on the other hand, was carried out entirely in Cornwall, most notably at smelters in Penzance, Hayle, Redruth, Truro and the St Austell area.

The Cornish Engine

Exploitation of Cornwall's rich mineral deposits during the 18th and 19th century would not have been possible without the massive reciprocating steam engines, or **beam engines**, with which the mines were worked. Principal among these were the pumping engines used to keep the mines free of water. To cope with this enormous task, the engines were of huge dimensions. Their steam cylinders were commonly 70-inches (1.78m) or more in diameter and the buildings in which they were housed were 60 feet (18.3m) or more in height with three floors or **chambers**. In keeping with the custom of the day, the engines were also built in grandiose style using massive cast iron fittings that were often finished with ornate neoclassical embellishments.

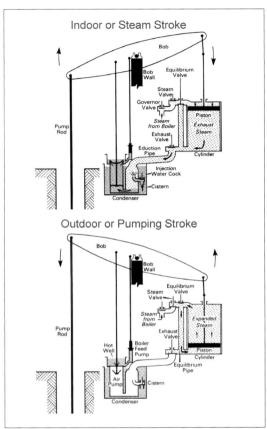

All beam pumping engines shared the same principle of reciprocation by which the power of the piston moving up and down in the steam cylinder was trans-mitted to the **pump rod** moving up and down in the shaft by way of a massive rocking beam or **bob** pivoted on the front wall of the engine house. Usually made of two pieces of cast iron up to 40 feet (12.2m) in length, this massive beam could weigh as much as 50 tons, so the front or **bob wall** of the engine house was very heavily constructed using dressed stone slabs to withstand the enormous load.

Similarly, to keep the cylinder firmly anchored amid the stresses generated by

Illustration of the steam cycle used to power a Cornish pumping engine. During the indoor or steam stroke, steam pressure is applied to the top of the piston in the cylinder while a vacuum is created beneath it. This drives the piston downwards and raises the pump rod in the shaft. During the outdoor or pumping stroke, the equilibrium valve is opened and the pressure on the piston is eliminated. This allows the piston to return to the top of the cylinder under the weight of the pump rods. The cycle is then repeated. In this way, the pumps operate under the downward force of the pump rods, whereas the power (steam) stroke of the engine simply lifts the pump rods for their next descent (modified from an original drawn for the Kew Bridge Engine Trust).

The three chambers of a Cornish pumping engine house as illustrated by Taylor's 90-inch pumping engine preserved at East Pool Mine between Camborne and Redruth. (a) The upper chamber showing the indoor end of the beam (bob) and catchwings. Note timber-shuttered front wall. (b) The middle chamber showing the top of the cylinder and the piston rod with bonnets for (from left to right) the governor, steam and equilibrium valves behind. (c) The lower chamber showing the base of the cylinder with its wood-insulated steam jacket, flanges covering pairs of holding down bolts, and the valve gear in the rear (2010).

the movement of the heavy bob, massive foundations (called **loadings**) and a substantial granite **bedstone** were needed to which the cylinder could be bolted. The

cylinder itself was double walled so that steam could be fed to the space between to create an insulating **steam jacket** that minimized heat loss. To ensure that the piston inside the cylinder moved up and down in a straight line, the **piston rod** connected to the indoor end of the bob was attached by way of an ingenious three-bar linkage known as the **parallel motion** that com-pensated for the curvilinear motion of the beam end.

The wooden pump rods attached to the other end of the bob extended to the bottom of the shaft where they operated plunger-type pumps that raised the water in a series of stages or **lifts**. The cast-iron pipe or **rising main** up which the water was raised either extended to the surface or, more frequently, to an underground **adit** level, down which the water could be drained by gravity to the nearest valley bottom or cliff base.

By the mid-19th century, pumping engines were almost entirely of Cornish design and manufacture, and the motion of steam in the cylinder followed the Cornish cycle. This is a **single-acting** cycle whereby the pressurized steam is moved from one side of the piston to the other before it is condensed. After the weight of the pump rods had brought the piston to the top of the cylinder, the **steam valve** was opened and steam admitted to the space above the piston under a pressure of some 40 pounds per square inch (psi). This drove the piston downwards, which closed the steam valve, allowing the steam to expand to complete the stroke. At the same time, the **exhaust valve** was opened which allowed the steam below the piston to escape by way of the **eduction pipe** to a separate **condenser** usually located outside the engine house at the base of the bob wall. The rapid condensation of the steam increased the downward force acting on the piston by creating a vacuum beneath it. As the piston approached the base of the cylinder, the exhaust valve was closed, trapping the remaining steam and bringing the piston to a stop. At this point the **equilibrium valve** (or Uncle Abraham valve as it was known to enginemen) was opened, which connected the space above the piston with that below. This eliminated the pressure on the piston, allowing it to return to the top of the cylinder under the weight of the pump rods. As the piston approached the top of the cylinder, closure of the equilibrium valve brought the piston to a stop once again. After a short pause, the steam valve was opened once more and the cycle was repeated. In this way, the pumps in the shaft were operated by the weight of the descending pump rods, not by the power stoke of the engine,

which simply raised the pump rods for their next descent.

Initially, all of the valve movements were controlled by the engine driver working the handles of the **valve gear** mounted in front of the cylinder on the ground floor or bottom chamber. Once a vacuum had been established in the condenser, however, the engine could be run automatically, the valves being opened and closed by the rise and fall of tappets attached to the **plug rod** (usually a pair) that hung from the bob. While continuing to monitor the engine, the driver was then free to oil its various moving parts, including the bearings on the outer end of the bob, which were accessed from the top chamber by way of two exterior boardwalks or **bob plats** on either side of the beam.

Cornish engines were typically operated at speeds of five to eight (double) strokes per minute. This rate was controlled by a water dashpot system or **cataracts** installed beneath the valve gear in the basement or **cockpit** of the engine house, and could be adjusted by the engine man to match the pumping demands on the engine. The engine man also operated the throttle valve or **governor**, which controlled the amount of steam introduced and, hence, the length of the stroke in the

The valve gear of Taylors's 90-inch pumping engine preserved at East Pool Mine. As the two vertical plug rods (centre) move up and down with the motion of the bob, they work the curved arms (with bright handles for manual operation) on the three horizontal rods or arbors. These, in turn, open and close the steam, exhaust and equilibrium valves. Under working conditions, the grey painted metalwork would have been bright (2010).

The beam or bob, bob plats, pump rod and bob wall of Taylor's 90-inch pumping engine at East Pool Mine. The rocking arm of the counterweight (balance box) in the foreground reuses the beam of a 36-inch pumping engine formerly at North Goonbarrow china clay pit, near Bugle (1967).

Two boilers illustrating the distinction between Cornish and Lancashire types. Left, a Cornish boiler with a single flue preserved at Harriett's shaft on Dolcoath Mine near Camborne (the boiler dates from the 1880's and was salvaged from Toldish Mine in Fraddon). Right, a Lancashire boiler with two flues preserved as an operational spare at the Crofton Pumping Station near Marlborough in Wiltshire (2010).

cylinder. In the event that the piston moved too far and threatened to strike the base of the cylinder, **catchwings** attached to the inner end of the bob were set to hit **striking blocks** on the top floor. These sat atop a shock absorbing system of timbers, the ends of which were embedded in the walls. The timbers comprised a massive **main girder** that extended across the engine house immediately behind the bob, and a pair of smaller **spring beams** that extended from end to end and continued out beyond the bob wall to support the bob plats.

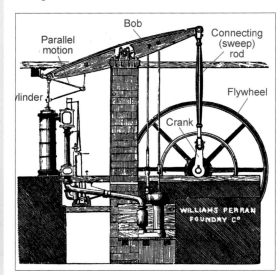

General arrangement of a rotative beam engine from the 1870 catalogue of the Williams' Perran Foundry. Here, rotary motion is achieved by linking the outdoor end of the bob to a crank and flywheel using a connecting (or sweep) rod.

Despite the weight and massive size of the machinery involved, surprisingly little energy was needed to raise the pump rod since the load was carefully counterbalanced. This was achieved by attaching a series of counterweights or **balance boxes** to the pump rod in such a way that the remaining unbalanced load was just sufficient to raise the water. Acting like seesaws with a box at one end filled with masonry and scrap, these balance boxes were attached at intervals down the shaft, sometimes with one at the shaft mouth, either parallel or at right angles to the engine house. A two-legged headgear or **shears** stood across the shaft mouth and was used for handling heavy equipment in the shaft. Supported by tie rods attached to the engine house, the shears carried a single pulley wheel over which a rope was fed from a manual or geared steam **capstan**.

Vital to the operation of the Cornish engine was a source of high-pressure steam. This was supplied by one or more coal-fired cylindrical boilers, typically 6 feet (1.8m) in diameter and 36 feet (11m) in length, arranged side-by-side in the **boiler house** alongside the engine house. The use of steam under high pressure was the single most important of Richard Trevithick's many innovations and the boilers he devised became known as **Cornish boilers** and were fitted with a single flue running the length of the boiler just below the centre line. **Lancashire boilers**, which later replaced the Cornish boiler, had a pair of such flues arranged side-by side. To increase efficiency, the boiler was usually encased in a brick sheath through which the flue gases were passed on their way to the chimney or **stack**, which was commonly attached to the corner of the engine house.

Since coal, which had to be imported from South Wales, was a significant expense, many of the improvements introduced by Trevithick and others Cornish engineers in the first half of the 18th century were designed to make the Cornish engine ever more efficient. Engine performance, or **duty**, was measured as the number of pounds of water raised one foot by a bushel (94 pounds) of coal, and records of this yardstick were published monthly. The competition this created between engineers resulted in dramatic improvements in engine duty, which rose from about 20 million pounds to 90 million pounds for the best engines between 1810 and 1840.

Rotative Beam Engines

Where beam engines were used for driving machinery, the reciprocal movement of the Cornish pumping engine was converted to a rotary motion by dispensing with the pump rod and coupling the outdoor end of the bob to a **crank** and **flywheel** by way of a **connecting rod** (or **sweep rod**). Although smaller and less powerful than pumping engines, with steam cylinders rarely more than 36-inches (0.9m) in diameter, these **rotative engines** were otherwise similar machines and were

View of the bob, bob plats, connecting rod, flywheel and paired winding drums of Michell's 30-inch beam winding engine preserved at East Pool Mine (2009).

housed in very similar, if smaller, buildings. They were, however, typically **double-acting** engines in which the steam was alternately admitted and exhausted both above and below the piston. In this way, steam power was used to force the piston up as well as down and cataracts for controlling the speed of the engine were unnecessary. But a heavy cast-iron flywheel with a diameter of 18 feet (5.5m) or more was required to keep the engine in motion. Unlike pumping engines, the valves were operated in all but the earliest rotative engines, not by the up-and-down movement of a plug rod attached to the bob, but by the forward-and-backward motion of a horizontal **eccentric rod** (usually two) attached to an eccentric on the crankshaft of the flywheel.

In Cornwall, rotative engines were most commonly employed either as winding

Archival photograph of New Stamps, a 36-inch stamping engine at Wheal Grenville, near Troon, showing bob, connecting rod, paired flywheels, camshaft and 136 heads of Cornish stamps. The auxiliary bob ahead of the flywheels pumped water for the dressing floors from a small shaft in front of the loadings.

Archival photograph of miners riding an inclined section of the man engine at the 234-fathom (428m) level of Dolcoath Mine, near Camborne, in 1893. Note the small platforms that the miners step on and off with each stroke.

engines (or **whims**) used for hoisting the ore out of the mine, or as stamping engines (or **stamps**) used to crush the ore to a fine sand prior to it's processing. In a whim, the crankshaft was linked to a winding drum from which one or two ropes extended over pulley wheels carried on a **headgear** over the shaft mouth to an ore bucket (known as a **kibble**) or bin (called a **skip**) in the shaft below. Not until the very end of the 19th century were whims fitted with **gigs** used to hoist men. In a stamps engine, the crankshaft was furnished with a pair of flywheels and drove a set of Cornish stamps. It did so by turning a long camshaft (on one or either side of the crankshaft loading) that lifted and then dropped rods shod with heavy iron heads onto an ore and water mixture fed into a box beneath.

Rotative engines could also be used to pump from distant shafts by means of a reciprocating line of horizontal **flat rods** worked by a pumping crank geared down from the crankshaft. These were supported on rocking arms or rollers to the shaft mouth where the backwards-and-forwards motion of the flat rods was converted to up-and-down motion in the shaft by way of a V-shaped rocking beam or **angle bob**. Not infrequently, rotative engines were employed to perform more than one function and, in small mines, it was not unknown for a single beam engine to pump, hoist and drive stamps.

On rare occasions, rotative engines were used as **man engines** to bring the miners to the surface. This was effected by utilizing the reciprocating motion of a wooden rod in the shaft, as it was for pumping. In this case, however, small platforms were attached to the rod onto which the miners could step on and step off at the beginning and end of each stroke. In this way, the miners were lifted in stages towards the surface each time the rod was raised by the engine.

Towards the end of the 19th century, rotative beam engines were progressively

replaced by **horizontal engines**, many of which were built by Holman Brothers of Camborne. In these engines, the cylinder was horizontal with the piston and connecting rods linked directly to the crank that turned the winding drum or, in a few cases, drove a man engine. Normally operated at higher steam pressures than beam engines, horizontal engines commonly had a pair of cylinders and were non-condensing, exhausting their steam, instead, directly to the atmosphere following colliery practice.

It is estimated that some 2,000 Cornish beam engines were installed in Britain in the 19th and early 20th centuries, mostly in Cornwall and Devon, and a further 500 or so were exported to mines and waterworks in the UK and around the world. Many of these were built at foundries in Cornwall, the most important of which were the Hayle Foundry of Harvey and Co., the nearby Copperhouse Foundry of Sandys, Carne and Vivian, and Williams Perran Foundry in Perranarworthal, between Truro and Falmouth. Smaller foundries also existed in St. Just, Camborne-Redruth, Charlestown, St. Blazey and elsewhere, and some Cornish engines were manufactured outside Cornwall, most notably at Mare's Foundry in Plymouth and Neath Abbey Foundry in South Wales.

Cornish Engine Houses
Although few Cornish beam engines have survived to the present day, much can be learned of their function from the engine houses that once contained them. These buildings were an integral part of the engines they housed and served both to support them and protect them from the elements. Because they were required to perform similar functions, all engine houses are of broadly similar design, but each was constructed specifically for the

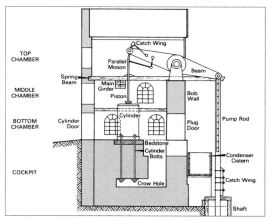

engine it was built to house. Although most are ruinous and almost all are well over a century old, the massive construction of these engine houses has ensured their survival and the longevity of many has been further enhanced as a result of their consolidation by local authorities.

Pumping Engine Houses
The largest engine houses were those used to house pumping engines because these engines had the largest cylinder

Elevation of a typical Cornish pumping engine house showing the three floor levels or chambers and basement or cockpit (from an original by the South Australian Department of Mines and Energy).

Main external features of a typical Cornish pumping engine house as illustrated by the 50-inch pumping engine preserved at Parkandillick China Clay Works near St. Dennis (1965).

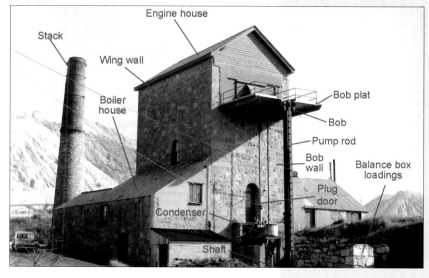

The boiler house side wall of John's 70-inch pumping engine house at Tywarnhayle Mine, near Porthtowan, showing openings (ascending from left to right) for the boiler house door, steam inlet, middle chamber window and main girder, with the drain opening at the wall's base. Note the arched plug door in the bob wall and the walling of the balance box pit in front of the shaft position (2010).

diameters, reaching up to 100-inches (2.5m), and piston strokes, ranging up to 11 feet (3.3m). A good example is the house of Taylor's 90-inch pumping engine preserved at East Pool Mine between Camborne and Redruth (see page 111).

All pumping engine houses were built beside the **engine shaft** they drained and so are easily recognized by the presence of a shaft or shaft collar at the foot of the front or **bob wall**. The engine house typically has three floors or chambers – a **bottom chamber**, the floor of which was more-or-less level with the base of the cylinder, a **middle chamber** with a floor level just below the top of the cylinder, and a **top chamber** supported by the main girder and spring beams at the level of the bob. A partial basement or **cockpit** in front of the cylinder loading contained the cataracts used to regulate the engine speed.

Because the bob wall supported the beam, which extended out over the shaft, it is the thickest wall of the engine house and is often built almost entirely of

dressed stone with only a single, usually stone-arched opening at the bottom chamber level. This is the **plug door**, which illuminated the valve gear in the bottom chamber and also permitted the engineman to gain access to the condensing work housed in a cistern at the foot of the bob wall outside. The base of the doorway also provided space for the eduction pipe that brought the spent steam to the condenser. The bob wall does not extend the full height of the house but only to the level where the blocks or **stools**, on which the axle or **trunnion** of the bob pivoted, were mounted. The space above was enclosed with timber shuttering, such that the upper side walls (or **wing walls**) are unsupported at their front ends.

The remaining walls of the engine house are less substantial and contain one or more brick-arched or linteled windows at each floor level. A much larger doorway at the bottom chamber level in the rear wall is the **cylinder opening** through which the cylinder and beam were originally brought into the house. This often served as the main entrance to the building. The rear wall, which typically has middle and upper chamber windows and is gable ended to support the roof, also contains a pair of small, sometimes bricked-in openings immediately beneath the top chamber. These supported the two spring beams that ran the length of the house and were cantilevered beyond the bob wall to support the bob plats.

In addition to windows, each of the side walls contains a smaller, sometimes bricked-in opening toward the rear of the house, the top of which is level with the floor of the top chamber. This supported the massive main girder that ran across the house immediately behind the bob and served as a shock absorber should the engine overstroke. Other openings in just one of the side walls betray the presence of a boiler house. These include the **boiler house door** adjacent to the bob wall in the bottom chamber, which permitted access to the boilers from the engine; the **steam inlet**, usually near the base of the wall, through which the steam pipe entered the engine house; and a smaller drain opening through which condensate from the steam jacket was fed back to the boilers.

The boilers themselves were typically housed in a single-floor, ridge-roofed or lean-to **boiler house** built against one side of the engine house. The size of the boiler house and the number of boilers it contained varied with the size of the engine, small engines requiring only a single boiler, whereas larger ones required several and big engines needed as many as five or six. In comparison with engine houses, however, boiler houses were quite lightly built and only a few have survived. But where they have not, their former position is usually revealed by the various boiler house openings in the adjacent side wall of the engine house.

To provide the fire tubes with sufficient draught, the boilers were linked by way of a flue to a substantial chimney or **stack**. This was usually built into the rear corner of the engine house to provide additional strength. However, free-standing stacks are not uncommon. Most are circular in cross section and built in two sections using stone to a height more-or-less level with the crest of the engine house roof, above which the taper is taken up in brickwork. In addition, some form of corbelling usually separates stonework from brickwork with additional brick corbelling near the chimney top.

Additional features of pumping engine houses commonly occur near the shaft mouth. These may include a walled or partially walled **condenser pit** at the foot of the bob wall that housed the condenser cistern, and an elongate **balance box pit**, usually in line with the engine house or at right angles to it, needed to accommodate the seesaw motion of the surface balance box.

Winding Engine Houses or Whims

Winding engine houses are similar to those of pumping engines, but tend to be smaller, some having just two chambers rather than the usual three. This is because the cylinder diameters of winding engines were usually 30-inches (0.8m) or less and the strokes correspondingly shorter. Winding engine houses are normally aligned with the shaft from which they hoisted and are easily distinguished from those of pumping

The house of the 24-inch winding engine at Wheal Hearle in Pendeen showing the crankshaft loading at the foot of the bob wall and a slot-like recess right of the plug door needed to accommodate the flywheel (2009).

Prominent slots for a crank (centre) and two flywheels in front of the plug door of the 36-inch New Stamps engine house at Wheal Grenville, near Troon. The left opening beside the plug door is for the eccentric rods used to operate the valve gear.

engines by the presence of a masonry **crankshaft loading** and a single deep slot or **flywheel pit** at the foot of the bob wall. A slot-like recess to accommodate the flywheel may also be present in the bob wall, along with openings for the eccentric rods that operated the valve gear from eccentrics on the crankshaft. If the engine was double acting, as most beam whims were, long holes for holding-down bolts needed to prevent the engine's up-stroke from lifting the beam out of its bearings may be evident toward the centre of the bob wall. A good example of a large winding engine house is that of Michell's 30-inch whim preserved at East Pool Mine between Camborne and Redruth (see page 113).

Some winding engines were entirely enclosed within their engine houses, with only the winding drum outside. Such **all-enclosed** engine houses lack a bob wall and have an elongate rectangular plan with the flywheel pit and crankshaft loading inside. The houses are typically two floored with an opening in the wall adjacent to the flywheel pit for the drum shaft. A good example is the all-enclosed house of the 27-inch whim preserved in steam at Levant Mine near Pendeen (see page 39).

Horizontal winding engines were housed in smaller single-storey brick or masonry buildings that were often quite lightly built. Where these have survived, they can usually be identified from the interior concrete or masonry foundations used to support the cylinder(s), flywheel and drum shaft.

Stamping Engine Houses or Stamps

Stamps engines closely resemble whims but were marginally larger, with cylinders up to 40-inches (1m) in diameter, and had two flywheels rather than one. Hence, the crankshaft loading of a stamps engine house has two flywheels pits, and a pair of slot-like recesses may be present in the bob wall. Level areas on one or both sides of the crankshaft loading are usually all that mark the site of the stamps themselves. To allow room for the stamps and the ore shoots that fed them, the boiler house was sometimes set across the rear of the building rather than alongside. Where this was the case, either the plug door served as the cylinder opening or the opening was moved to one of the side walls. In other cases, the rear wall was used to support an **auxiliary bob**, or **back bob**, that was linked to the indoor end of the main bob and used to pump water needed for the ore treatment process from a shallow shaft behind the engine house. Alternative arrangements that were sometimes used for the same purpose involved either an auxiliary bob set low down in front of the crankshaft loading and worked by twin rods from the nose of the beam (see page 14), or a pump set in the, or a pump set in the loading behind the crankshaft and worked by a rod from the beam.

Because crushing was the first step in the treatment process, stamps engine houses were usually sited at the top of a slope so that the crushed ore could be gravity fed to **dressing floors** below. Although rarely marked by structures, the sites of dressing floors are often revealed by pits and circular depressions that identify the location of settling tanks and rotating **buddles** that were used to separate the heavier ore from the unwanted, lighter waste.

Other Structures

In addition to engine houses, a variety of other structures may mark the sites of former mines, particularly those active in the late 19th and early 20th centuries. While beyond the scope of this guide, those associated with arsenic production are sufficiently common to warrant special mention.

Before the ore could be shipped to the smelters, it had to roasted in order to drive off impurities that interfered with the smelting process. This was carried out in a burning house or **calciner**. Towards the end of the 19th century, however, one of these impurities, arsenic, had become a valuable commodity in its own right, principally as an insecticide. As a result, the production of arsenic became important as a byproduct of the mining process, often prolonging the life of the mine after metalliferous mining declined. To recover the arsenic, the fumes produced in the calciner were passed through a long flue, on the walls of which the arsenic condensed as crystals that could be collected. Structures associated with this process include small square buildings,

The Brunton calciner at Wheal Busy, near Chacewater, with its distant arsenic stack at the head of the flue labyrinth. The arsenic concern was installed during the mine's last reworking in 1909 (1967).

called **Brunton calciners**, in which the ore was roasted on a rotating grill; the meandering flue or **labyrinth** into which the fumes passed; and the solitary chimney or **arsenic stack** to which the flue led.

A final structure that, in many cases, has survived intact is the mine accounts building, or **count house**, from which the miners were paid and where the shareholders periodically met. Like office buildings today, these were commonly symbolic of the mine's success. Hence, they are often rather attractive buildings made of dressed stone in Georgian architectural style, and their survival owes its origin to their frequent reuse as dwellings. For smaller mines a timber count house was often sufficient.

As a result of its conversion to a dwelling, the count house of Wheal Providence (and childhood home of the lead author) in Carbis Bay has survived after all other traces of the mine have been lost to urban development (2009).

Fox's whim, a picturesque engine house at the foot of Trencrom Hill, was erected beside Mitchell's shaft at Trencrom Mine (later part of Wheal Sisters) in 1871 for a 60-inch pumping engine. Its name, however, comes from its subsequent reuse as the house of a 24-inch winding engine that hoisted from Fox's shaft across the fields to the south (left). Plans are presently afoot to convert the engine house into a dwelling (2009).

CHAPTER 2 St. Ives – Morvah Mining District

The St. Ives-Morvah mining district runs WSW from St. Ives along the north coast of West Penwith adjacent to the St. Ives-St. Just road (B3306), and south from St. Ives towards Nancledra along the old Penzance road (B3311). The district was both a tin-producing and copper-producing area along the northern margin of the Land's End granite, the boundary of which more-or-less parallels the B3306 just inland of the coast before curving SE inland of St. Ives and Carbis Bay. Mines lying close this boundary, such as Gurnard's Head, Trevega Bal and Providence, produced tin and/or copper,

whereas those further inland, such as Ding Dong and Giew, lay entirely within the granite and were solely tin producers. The mining district is not part of the Mining Landscape World Heritage Site and many of its surviving engine houses, which mostly lie between the B3306 and the coast, or are clustered around the hills of Trink and Trencrom, are ruinous and have not been consolidated. All lie close to roads or can be reached by public footpath, but permission should be sought wherever access requires private land to be crossed.

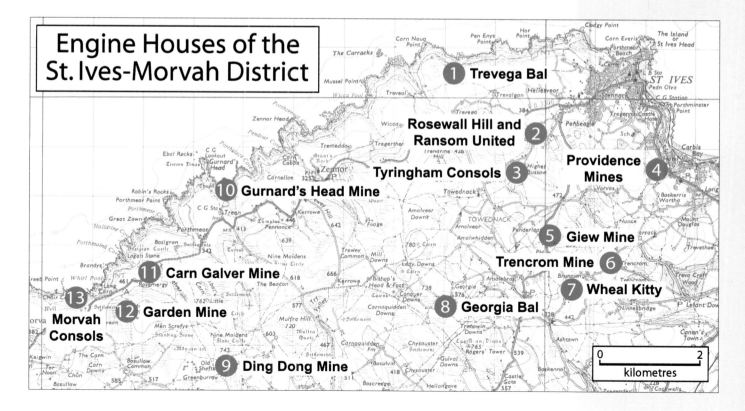

Engine Houses of the St. Ives-Morvah District

Two views of the stamps engine house at Trevega Bal (2009 and 1965)

1. TREVEGA BAL (SW481405)

Standing as a lone sentinel on the cliffs between St. Ives and Zennor, is the ruinous stamps engine house of Trevega Bal. The stamps probably date from 1869 when this

ancient group of small and intermittently productive tin and copper mines (reputedly started by Matthew Oates in 1674) was worked for a few years as West St. Ives Consols. However, the original house may date to 1859 when the mine (worked as Brea Consols) was drained by a 36-inch engine that also drove eight heads of Cornish stamps. This might account for the unusual position of the stack, which is attached to the west end of the bob wall, and the location of a walled shaft in-line with the house a short distance to the SSE that suggests the engine also worked flat rods. A deep slot in the bob wall marks the position of the flywheel, whereas the openings beneath the plug door are for the two rods that operated the engine's valve gear from eccentrics on the crankshaft. The engine's boiler house (large enough for two boilers) lay alongside to the west where there is a flue hole at the base of the stack and openings for the steam inlet and drain in the wall of the engine house. The mine reached a depth of 50 fathoms (91m) below sea level and is reputedly where blasting was first introduced to West Cornwall around 1700. It was last worked just prior to World War I. The base of the mine's 16-inch pumping engine house and separate stack lie on the cliffs to the north (SW481408).

2. ROSEWALL HILL AND RANSOM UNITED (SW496393)

On the east side of Rosewall Hill, overlooking St. Ives, two small chimneys and two very ruinous engine houses mark the site of Rosewall Hill and Ransom United mine. Hidden amid a thicket some distance below the chimneys is the bob wall of the pumping engine house on

Great Ransom shaft (SW497394). This housed a 40-inch engine built by the Copperhouse Foundry of Sandys, Vivian and Co. that was bought secondhand from Wheal Trenwith in St. Ives in 1857 when a new mine was established by amalgamating the older Rosewall Hill Mine and Wheal Ransom, some of the workings of which date to the 16th century. For several years following the closure of this productive tin mine in 1876, by which time its had reached a depth of 182 fathoms (333m), the engine continued to pump the northern (Goole Pellas) section of the mine by way of flat rods. Although the bob wall is now heavily overgrown, the recess that housed the condenser cistern and the fine stone collar built to secure the top of the shaft in 1857 can still be seen through the plug door. The slot and pit for the balance box, from which the flat rods would have extended, are prominent features on the NE side of the shaft. The boiler house formerly lay alongside to the NE. Some 50 yards further north lies the overgrown base of the mine's 22-inch whim.

Amid woodlands lower down the hill is the ruinous and heavily overgrown house of the mine's 32-inch stamps engine (SW499393), which was also bought from Wheal Trenwith and set to work in 1858. A portion of the bob wall has fallen to reveal the cockpit ahead of the cylinder loading inside the house. Footings for a boiler house large enough for two boilers extend behind the house on the SE side. The engine continued to be used as part of Goole Pellas and was offered for sale (as a 30-inch) in 1881.

The two prominent chimneys higher on the hillside date from an earlier working of the mine (as Rosewall Hill and Gweans Mining Company) and are thought to be those of a 36-inch pumping engine built by Harvey and Co. of Hayle in 1838 (lower) and a 20-inch Boulton and Watt whim (upper). Both engines were offered for sale when the mine closed in 1842.

Bob wall of the pumping engine house on Great Ransom shaft at Rosewall Hill and Ransom United mine (1964).

Cylinder loading and cockpit of the stamps engine house at Rosewall Hill and Ransom United mine seen through the fallen bob wall (2009).

Interior of the pumping engine house at Tyringham Consols showing the bob wall (left), the boiler house side wall and part of the rear wall (2009).

3. TYRINGHAM CONSOLS (SW494385)

On the southern slopes of Rosewall Hill, at Bussow Farm, stand the remains of the 40-inch pumping engine house of Tyringham Consols. This engine was erected in 1880 during the last reworking of this minor tin mine under the name West Providence. Also known as Bussow, the mine acquires its name from an earlier reworking in 1860-64. The engine, which was erected on a new shaft that remains open, also operated a long line of flat rods to pump

older workings across the fields to the south. The mine closed in 1883. The engine house was partially destroyed for building material around 1925. The boiler house for the engine's two boilers stood beside the standing south wall, which preserves the roofline and has openings for the boiler house door and steam inlet. The base of the stack is attached to the NW corner.

4. PROVIDENCE MINES (SW523384)

Until their removal in the 1970s to make way for a housing estate, the impressive dressed-granite engine house on Higgs' shaft, and the shaft's large burrow of mine tailings, were prominent remains in Carbis Bay of this once-important tin and copper mine. The engine house was erected in 1865 for a 40-inch pumping engine built by Sandys, Vivian and Co. of Copperhouse. The projecting north corner of the bob wall bore the inscription "WH 1865", probably in reference to William Hollow, the mine manager. The mine was established in 1832 with the merger of Wheal Providence and a number of smaller workings (some dating to the 16th century), and became one of the richest in the district, as its fine surviving count house at Chy-an-Gweal (now used as a dwelling) bears witness (see page 19). The mine had 500 employees in 1870, but closed in 1877, by which time Higgs' shaft had reached a depth of over 200 fathoms (366m). Footings of the pumping engine house on the Old Providence section of the mine (probably that of a 30-inch engine at work in 1838 and offered for sale in 1847) survive on the cliff above the mine's adit at the west end of Carbis Bay Beach (SW524390).

Higgs' 40-inch pumping engine house at Providence Mines viewed from the top of the mine's prominent burrow prior to the area's redevelopment for housing (1967).

Engine house and boiler house wall of Frank's 50-inch pumping engine at Giew Mine (2009).

5. GIEW MINE (SW500373)

The conserved engine house at Giew mine forms a prominent landmark alongside the old St. Ives-Penzance road (B3311) near Cripplesease. This housed a 50-inch pumping engine erected on Frank's shaft in 1871 as part of a reworking started in 1869 under the name South Providence. An inscription on the bob wall reads "SP 1871". By that time the shaft was already 142 fathoms (260m) below adit, the mine having been previously worked for tin under various names (1820-25 and 1859-65 as Durlo Mine, 1836-1858 as Reeth Consolidated, and 1865-67 as Billia Consols). The earliest records of mining activity at Giew date to 1713-15. The pumping engine, which came from Wheal Daniell near Chacewater in 1873, was purchased from Harvey and Co. of Hayle (who provided a new beam) and remained on site until 1889, although the mine closed in 1877. Adjoining the house to the west are the walls of the boiler house, which contained two boilers. The small hillock some distance north of the engine house is all that remains of the 22-inch whim that wound from the same shaft. Between 1908 and 1923, the mine was worked as part of St. Ives Consols. Frank's shaft was sunk to its final depth of 244 fathoms (446m) and the engine house was converted for use as an ore bin. Heavily overgrown remains of the extensive milling plant, twin calciners and square calciner stack erected at that time lie across the B3311 0.5 km to the SW (SW497370).

Fox's whim and boiler house (left) at Trencrom Mine, later part of Wheal Sisters (2009).

Two views of the pumping engine house at Wheal Kitty taken in 2009 and 1966.

6. TRENCROM MINE (WHEAL SISTERS)
(SW513367)

On the NW side of Trencrom Hill is the well-preserved engine house known locally as Fox's whim. This house preserves an interesting history that reveals its earlier use for a pumping engine. It was originally erected in 1871 on Mitchell's shaft (then 250m deep) by Eustace and Son of Hayle for a 60-inch pumping engine that was set to work in 1872. But at some point following the tin mine's incorporation into the Wheal Sisters group in 1875, the house was re-used for a 24-inch rotative engine that wound from Fox's shaft across the field to the south. To do so, a flywheel slot was cut into the bob wall and the prominent flywheel loading was built across the shaft, the stone arch for which is visible beneath them. Because of the location of Fox's shaft, the pit for the winding drum is angled at about 45° to the flywheel and was presumably driven by bevel gears. This ingenious re-use is clearly evident in the existing layout of the loadings. The cylinder bedstone and boiler house for a single boiler (on the west side) are those of the whim. The house was purchased at auction in 2008 with plans to convert it into a dwelling (see also page 20).

7. WHEAL KITTY (WHEAL SISTERS)
(SW505362)

On the south side of Trink Hill, near Brunnion, stands the ruinous house of a small pumping engine beside Mushell's shaft in the Wheal Kitty section of Wheal Sisters. The house is likely to be that of a

28-inch engine, which was at work on this profitable tin mine in 1864, when the shaft was already 190 fathoms (347m) deep, and which is listed in an 1890 prospectus. The engine's single boiler was housed on the east side with the square stack partially built into the SE corner of the engine house. Already productive for copper in the 1840s, the mine was worked briefly (without stoppage) as Polpeor in 1873-74 before being amalgamated in 1875 with its neighbours Wheal Margaret, Wheal Mary and Trencrom Mine as part of the Wheal Sisters group. Wheal Sisters closed in 1890, but was briefly reopened in 1906-08.

8. GEORGIA BAL (SW481357)

At Baker's Pit, a china clay working to the west of Nancledra, stands the consolidated, all-enclosed engine house referred to locally as Georgia Bal. Baker's Pit was an amalgamation of several earlier china clay workings taken up by William K. Baker in 1868-69. The engine house, which served the pit, was built by the Nicholls family of masons and housed a 25-inch rotative beam engine purchased secondhand in 1874 from Trelyon Consols, near St. Ives, where it had been worked as a multipurpose pumping, winding and stamping engine since the 1850s. A well-preserved lean-to boiler house extends beyond the rear of the engine house on its south side and housed a single boiler. After World War I, the house was modified to accommodate an electric winder (the drum of which remains in situ) that operated until the now-flooded pit was closed in 1942. Baker's Pit was gifted to the Cornwall Wildlife trust in 2000.

Two views of the engine house at Georgia Bal (2009 and 1967). The lower photo shows the drum of the electric winder and the adjoining (roofless) boiler house. The roofed building to the right is a later addition.

Two views of the 40-inch pumping engine house on Greenburrow shaft at Ding Dong Mine taken before and after its consolidation in the late 1980s (1966 and 2009).

with tales of a visit by Joseph of Arimathea and the young Jesus in Roman times, and records that date to the beginning of the 17th century. In its final form, the mine was active between 1820 and 1877, and its burrows were reworked in 1912-15.

Greenburrow Pumping Engine (SW434344)

The consolidated house of Greenburrow pumping engine forms a prominent landmark that can be seen on the skyline for miles. It was erected on older burrows beside Greenburrow shaft (now covered with a grating) by Elisha Marks in 1864, and housed a 40-inch pumping engine built by Harvey and Co. of Hayle in 1857. This engine had previously been in use at Ding Dong (North Killiow) shaft some 600m to the NW, and continued to pump from this shaft using flat rods attached to the balance box, the slot and pit for which are visible on the NW side of the shaft. The house still contains the cylinder bedstone (with four bolts) and was conserved in the late 1980s. The outline of the house for the engine's two boilers is visible on the east side.

Ishmael's Whim (SW443348)

In the eastern part of the Ding Dong sett stands the house of a 25-inch winding engine house known as Ishmael's whim. The alignment of the house suggests that it wound from Tredinneck shaft some 250m to the east, although it doubtless wound from others. The masonry loadings with conspicuous bolt tunnels in front of the house are those of the crankshaft and flywheel, and the prominent buttress beside them supported the winding drum. The recess in the loadings at the foot of

9. DING DONG MINE

On the high moors east of the Madron-Morvah road, no less than three engine houses mark the site of the famous tin mine known as Ding Dong. The mine is reputedly one of the oldest in Cornwall

Two views of the 25-inch winding engine known as Ishmael's whim at Ding Dong Mine (1966 and 2009).

the bob wall housed the condenser cistern and the two brick-lined openings alongside the plug door are those for the rods that operated the engine's valve gear from eccentrics on the crankshaft. The outline of the house of the engine's single boiler is clearly visible on the north side.

Tredinneck Pumping Engine (SW444348)
Beside the road some 250m due east of Ishmael's whim stands one of the oldest engine houses in the district. The house is that of a long-lived 30-inch pumping engine erected on Tredinneck shaft in 1825 and worked until the mine closed in 1878, by which time the shaft was 135

Two views of the 30-inch pumping engine on Tredinneck shaft at Ding Dong Mine (1966 and 2009).

The house of the 30-inch pumping engine at Gurnard's Head Mine (2009)

fathoms (245m) deep. The engine had a single boiler housed on the east side and also pumped from Providence shaft, some 200m to the NW, by way of flat rods attached to the balance box on the west side of the shaft. The solidly built house incorporates stones from a prehistoric stone circle and, like all the surviving engine houses at Ding Dong, lacks a gable end and had a hipped roof. On the north side of the road, about half way between Ishmael's whim and Tredinnick engine house are the ruins of the mine's count house.

10. GURNARD'S HEAD (NORTH UNITED) MINE (SW435382)

On the cliffs at Treen Cove, on the east side of Gurnard's Head, stands the dramatically positioned engine house of Gurnard's Head or North United Mine, an unsuccessful copper working known earlier as Wheal Treen. The mine was worked as Gurnard's Head Mine in 1834-43, but the ruinous engine house is that of a 30-inch pumping engine built by Harvey and Co. of Hayle in 1843 and erected on South shaft (which is still open) in 1844 when the mine was restarted under the name North United. Offered for sale in 1847, the engine was bought back by Harvey and Co., and sold to Guadalcanal Mine in Spain in 1848. The house of the engine's single boiler lay along the NE side, served by a separate stack, the base of which lies behind the engine house to the SE. South shaft reached a depth of 80 fathoms (146m) below adit.

11. CARN GALVER MINE (SW422365)

Standing picturesquely beside the St. Ives-St. Just road (B3306) west of Carn Galver are the two engine houses of Carn Galver Mine. These housed a 22-inch winding engine and, to the south, a 30-inch pumping engine, both of which were erected in 1871 during the last (1871-75) working of this intermittently productive tin mine. The mine had previously been active in 1850-69 as a reworking of the older Morvah and Zennor United (1835-40). Both engines, at least one of which was purchased from Harvey and Co. of Hayle, had single boilers housed, respectively, on the east side of the whim and the north side of the pumping engine house where the walls are well preserved. The loadings in front of the winding engine are those of the flywheel and winding drum, which wound back-to-front from the engine shaft behind the house. The bob wall of the pumping engine house has been brought down to fill the shaft, which had reached a depth of 130 fathoms (238m) when the mine closed. Both engine houses were conserved by the National Trust in 1984. The mine's fine count house, or office building, survives as a dwelling to the north of the whim.

Two views of the engine houses of the 22-inch winding engine (left) and 30-inch pumping engine (right) at Carn Galver Mine taken before and after their consolidation in 1984 (1966 and 2009).

Two views of the 30-inch pumping engine house at Garden or Morvah Hill Mine (2010 and 2009).

12. GARDEN (MORVAH HILL) MINE (SW416357)

High on Watch Croft, south of Rosemergy, stands the prominent bob wall of a 30-inch pumping engine house erected at Garden or Morvah Hill Mine in 1861 during a reworking of this briefly productive tin mine. The engine had been purchased secondhand from Wheal Trebarvah, near Perranuthnoe, in 1860. Flush with the bob wall on the NE side is the more lightly built front wall of the boiler house, which held a single boiler. The mine closed in 1870 by which time the still-open shaft had been sunk at least 61 fathoms (112m).

13. MORVAH CONSOLS (SW407359)

On Trevowhan Cliffs, NE of Morvah, lie the scant remains of a multipurpose engine house erected in 1873 during the last (1871-74) significant working of this unsuccessful tin mine. This housed a 24-inch single-acting rotative engine built at the Copperhouse Foundry of Sandys, Vivian and Co. It had been bought secondhand from Balleswidden Mine, near St. Just, equipped with a new cylinder cast by Nicholas Holman's foundry in Tregeseal. The engine was set to work in March, 1874, and was used for both pumping and stamping. The house, which has fallen to the level of the cylinder loading and cockpit, faces SW with a flywheel slot and part of the plug

Two views of the multipurpose 24-inch engine house at Morvah Consols, the view on the left showing the bob wall (left) and the house of the engine's single boiler on the SW side (right) in 1967 and 2009.

door in the bob wall. Pumping from Hammond's shaft at the rear of the house was achieved by way of an auxiliary "back bob" supported on the rear wall. The house of the engine's single boiler lay alongside to the SW, the footings of which survive. Hammond (Engine) shaft, which remains open, was worked to a depth of 26 fathoms (47m).

The engine houses of the dramatic Crowns section of Botallack Mine, near Pendeen. The lower house is that of a 30-inch pumping engine built by Harvey and Co. of Hayle and erected new on Crowns Engine shaft in 1835. The upper house is Pearce's all-enclosed 24-inch winding engine moved to this site in 1862 to hoist from the then-new Boscawen diagonal shaft in the cliff below (2009).

CHAPTER 3 **Pendeen – St. Just Mining District**

The rich Pendeen-St. Just mining district lies on the west coast of West Penwith between Pendeen Watch and Cape Cornwall. The district was both a tin- and copper-producing area along the western margin of the Land's End granite, the boundary of which runs NW-SE between the St. Ives-St. Just road (B3306) and the coast. Mines along the coast, such as Levant, Botallack and Wheal Owles, lie in greenstone and slate, and were producers of tin and/or copper. They were generally richer than the mines further inland, which lie entirely within the granite and were predominantly tin producers and less profitable. The district is unusual in that most of its lodes run NW-SE, broadly perpendicular to both their usual orientation and that of the coastline. The district is also thought to be one of the first to try underground tin mining and later pioneered mining beneath the sea with levels extending out 1.6 km from the shore and over 600m below the seabed. Its rapid growth into a major mining area occurred in the early decades of the 19th century, but was short lived with decline setting in by the 1860s with falling copper prices. Tin mining, however, continued into the 20th century and Geevor Mine (formerly North Levant)

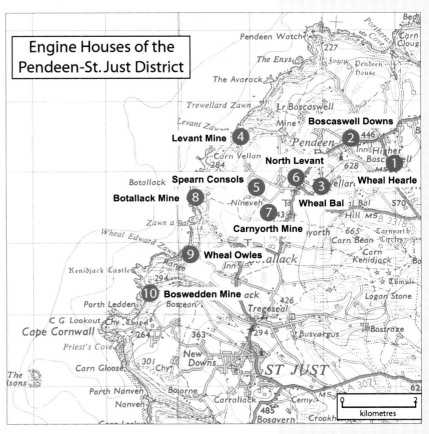

Engine Houses of the Pendeen-St. Just District

was worked until 1990. The mine is now an important museum of 20th century mining technology.

Two views of the 30-inch multipurpose engine house at Wheal Hearle from the front (top) with the whim engine house behind, and from the rear (below) showing the flywheel slot and opening for the auxiliary "back bob" in the rear wall. The walls extending to the right in the lower view are those of the boiler house (2009).

1. WHEAL HEARLE (EAST BOSCASWELL MINE) (SW390341)

Standing prominently beside the B3318 immediately south of Pendeen are the two engine houses of Wheal Hearle or North Boscaswell Mine. The larger (and more easterly) of the two housed the mine's multipurpose 30-inch pumping/stamping engine erected on Borlase's shaft in 1860. The smaller house is that of the mine's 24-inch whim, which wound from Skip shaft to the NW. From 1864 this was the mine's deepest shaft, ultimately reaching 150 fathoms (274m). Worked between 1855 and 1866, the mine was a minor producer of tin and a little copper. The arrangement of the pumping/stamping engine is unique among surviving engine houses in that, contrary to the usual practice, the main beam lifted the pump rods in the

The engine house of the 36-inch pumping engine at Boscaswell Downs Mine in the process of being converted into a barn. The abutting building is a private house (1967).

now-filled shaft (SE of which are the loadings for the balance box), while the stamps were driven by an auxiliary "back bob" supported on the rear wall, which contains a prominent slot for the flywheel. To make room for the stamps (initially 15 but increased to 21 in 1861 and 24 in 1862), the boiler house for the engine's single boiler is arranged at right angles to the engine house with the boiler house door and steam inlet at the rear of the building immediately in front of the attached stack. The whim is more conventional with loadings for the flywheel and drum at the base of the bob wall, which contains a deep flywheel slot, and the boiler house for the engine's single boiler alongside to the SE (see page 17).

2. BOSCASWELL DOWNS MINE (SW384344)

Adjoining a private dwelling alongside the B3306 in Pendeen, but largely hidden from the street, is the house of the 36-inch pumping engine of Boscaswell Downs Mine. At work on the mine in 1864, the engine was offered for sale in 1875. The bases of two more engine houses (probably those of the 34-inch stamps engine and 24-inch whim also at work in 1864) lie in the overgrown triangle of land to the west. The mine is an ancient one and was already nearly 200 fathoms (366m) deep in 1838. But it reached its heyday between 1852 and 1874, when it was worked for both tin and copper. The mine was re-opened in 1906 as Boscaswell United and worked largely unsuccessfully until 1910, during which time a mill was

Front view of the 21-inch pumping engine house at Wheal Bal (converted to a barn) showing the filled bob opening and plug door in the bob wall, the roof of the probable boiler house alongside and the count house behind (2010).

3. WHEAL BAL (SW381337)

On the edge of the common just east of Trewellard, is the engine house of Wheal Bal. Reduced in height and converted long ago into a barn, the house is that of a 21-inch pumping engine offered for sale (together with a 24-inch stamps) in 1861. The engine had an unusually short indoor stroke of only 6 feet. The adjoining sty probably makes use of the house of the engine's single boiler and the granite building being renovated to the north is likely to be the mine's count house. Another ancient mine (records of which date to 1690), Wheal Bal was worked for tin between 1852 and 1862, but was never very productive.

4. LEVANT MINE

On the cliffs below Trewellard stand the engine houses of Levant Mine, the greatest of all the mines in the district. The history of this famous copper, tin and,

erected on Boscaswell Downs that included a Merton roasting furnace, substantial remains of which still exist (SW380351). This type of burning house was multi-hearthed and used rotating arms to stir the ore as it was roasted to remove impurities. Intermittent activity at Boscaswell United continued until 1922.

Quintessential view of Levant Mine taken in 1967, showing the derelict house and former stack of the pumping engine, and the preserved all-enclosed whim. The chimneys in the background are those of the arsenic flue (left) and stamps engine (right).

Levant Mine in 2009, showing the house of the 45-inch pumping engine with the arsenic flue chimney behind, and the all-enclosed 40-inch whim now restored and worked under steam by the National Trust. The headgear stands over Skip shaft.

later, arsenic mine spans 110 years from 1820 until 1930, with records of mining activity dating back a further 150 years. At the time of its closure, the mine had reached a depth of 350 fathoms (640m) and had been worked over a mile (1.6 km) beneath the sea. The mine's output amounted to some 24,000 tons of black tin, 130,000 tons of 10% copper ore and 4000 tons of arsenic.

Pumping Engine and Whim (SW368345)

On the cliff edge stand the elderly engine houses of the mine's 45-inch pumping engine and all-enclosed 27-inch whim, both built by Harvey and Co. of Hayle, the latter to the design of Francis Mitchell. The pumping engine house was built in 1835 for a new 40-inch engine, but a larger cylinder was added in 1872 and the engine's bob broke and had to be replaced in 1891. The balance box pit on the SE side of the house sits adjacent to the former position of the boiler house, which held two boilers. The whim, which originally had a 24-inch cylinder, dates from 1840 and hoisted from the 278-fathom (508m) level of Skip shaft beside the main Engine shaft. After the mine closed, the engine was preserved and later returned to steam by the Trevithick Society. Together with its conserved house and rebuilt boiler house, which originally had a taller stack, the engine is now the property of the National Trust (see page 4). The two stacks to the east of these engine houses are those of the arsenic flue (nearer the cliff) and 32-inch stamps engine, only the base of which survives.

The engine house and separate stack of the horizontal man engine as it looked in 1967 when some of the walls were still standing.

Two views of the 35-inch multipurpose (winding and pumping) engine house at Higher Bal, Levant (1967 and 2009). The loadings in front of the bob wall are those of the winding drum and flywheel, and (on the right side) the flat rod crank and gearing. The flat rods ran SE from the house to Guide shaft (at camera position left). The roofline of the boiler house can be seen on the north side wall (right).

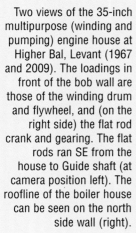

Man Engine (SW368344)

Inland, some 150m south of Engine shaft, is the base of the engine house and the decorative stack of the horizontal engine used to drive the Levant man engine. The man engine (a device used in deep mines to raise and lower miners in the shaft, see page 14) was installed in 1857, but the 20-inch beam engine originally used to drive it was replaced by a compound horizontal engine with 18-inch and 30-inch cylinders in 1893. This was geared to the man engine in the now-secured shaft a short distance to the ENE by way of flat rods attached at either end to balance boxes, the loadings and pits for which can still be seen. The engine's two boilers lay in the depressed area east of the stack on the other side of the house. An underground passage running due north from the top of the shaft, which was worked to the 266-fathom (486m) level, took the miners up a granite spiral stairway directly to the miners' dry, the floor and in-built bathtubs of which can be seen on the far side of the road. It was here on the 20th October 1919, that the failure of the man engine's main rod caused the death of 31 miners.

Higher Bal Multipurpose Engine (SW370340)

Beside Levant Road, inland towards Trewellard, stands the well-preserved

multipurpose engine house of Higher Bal or Higher Levant. Erected in 1887, the building housed a 35-inch rotative engine that wound and pumped in Guide shaft (covered with a grating some 30m to the SW) until the mine closed in 1930. The engine had previously been used to drive stamps at Spearn Consols (of which Guide shaft was part) and was included in the sale of this mine to Levant in 1880. Pits for the flywheel and winding drum are visible in front of the house, the crankshaft additionally operating pumps by way of a short run of flat rods on the SE side, the footings for which are visible between the house and the shaft. Pits for the balance boxes attached at either end of the flat rods to counteract the weight of the pump rods lie beside the house and the shaft. The house of the engine's single boiler lay along the seaward side.

5. SPEARN CONSOLS/SPEARN MOOR MINE
(SW371337)

Across the fields to the SSE of Higher Bal is the diminutive engine house of Spearn Consols. This ruin is thought to be the house of an 18-inch winding engine offered for sale in 1878. Spearn Consols was a small tin mine active in 1853-73 and, before that (as Wheal Spearn) in 1811. In 1874, the mine was amalgamated with neighbouring Spearn Moor Mine before being swallowed up by Levant. The large plug door evidently served as the cylinder opening since the stack is built entirely inside the SW corner of the rear wall. The walling alongside to the SW is that of the boiler house, which held a single boiler. The base of a rotative engine house at Spearn Moor, 400m to the NW

(SW368339) is thought to be that of the multipurpose 35-inch stamps engine later re-erected at Higher Bal. The stack to the SW (SW369336) belonged to a rotative pumping and winding engine on Nineveh shaft of Carnyorth Mine, which became part of Botallack.

The diminutive 18-inch winding engine house at Spearn Consols as it appeared in 1967 (with Higher Bal in the background) and 2009 (below). The ivy-covered walling to the rear of the building is that of the boiler house.

The base of the house of the multipurpose 24-inch engine at North Levant Mine after removal of the surrounding burrow, showing its attached stack and flue opening (2010).

6. NORTH LEVANT MINE (SW376337)

Just west of the St. Ives-St. Just road (B3306) in the village of Trewellard is the base of the house of a 24-inch multipurpose (pumping and winding) engine. This engine worked Law's shaft (a short distance to the NE) on the eastern (or East Levant) section of North Levant Mine. The mine was a productive tin and subordinate copper concern between 1854 and 1891, and was at work before this as

Wheal Stennack and East Levant. The sett became part of Geevor Mine in 1892 and finally closed in 1913. Part of the side wall of the condenser cistern projects from the base of the bob wall. The house of the engine's single boiler lay alongside to the NW on the opposite (flue hole) side to the attached stack.

7. CARNYORTH MINE (SW372334)

In the fields west of Carnyorth, the base of the house of a rotative engine marks the site of Carnyorth Mine, a small tin mine active from 1852 until 1866 when it was merged with Botallack. The house is probably that of a 24-inch stamps and winding engine at work in 1865. The base of the stack is attached to the NE corner. In the small industrial area some 100m to the east, the base of a pumping engine house in-line with the whim is likely to be that of Pearce's 30-inch engine erected by George Eustice in 1852 in just 13 days. Pearce's shaft reached the 136-fathom (248m) level below adit at 20 fathoms (37m).

8. BOTALLACK MINE (SW362335)

Best known of all Cornish engine houses are those dramatically perched on the cliffs below Botallack in the Crowns section of legendary Botallack Mine. The lower house is that of Crowns 30-inch pumping engine built by Harvey and Co. of Hayle, which drained this section of the mine from 1835 until 1895 when flooding forced this famous old copper, tin and, later, arsenic mine to close. The engine house contains the cylinder bedstone and a short stack built inside the west corner to save space. The boiler house on the NW side is unusual in that it held two boilers

The base of the rotative engine house at Carnyorth Mine (2010).

of unequal size. The now-filled Crowns Engine shaft was 135 fathoms (247m) deep. The mine was already being worked beneath the sea in 1778 and was reopened unsuccessfully between 1906 and 1914, although the Crowns section was not included. The extensive remains at the top of the cliff, which include dressing floors, a well-preserved calciner, labyrinth and arsenic stack, a power station, and a fine count house, mostly date from this latter period of reworking. Allen shaft, over which a headgear still stands, was also sunk at this time. The headgear was erected in the 1980s in anticipation of underground development between Allen shaft and Geevor Mine's Victory shaft. But this never happened. Production from Botallack Mine amounts to some

Two views of the Crowns section of Botallack Mine taken before and after consolidation of the lower 30-inch pumping engine house and upper all-enclosed 24-inch whim in 1984-85. Upper view is taken above Boscawen shaft with Wheal Owles in the background (1964). Lower view shows the base of the whim's boiler house and the loadings for the winding drum (2009).

Consolidated 36-inch pumping engine house of the Cargodna (West Wheal Owles) section of Wheal Owles. The engine house of Pearce's all-enclosed whim and headgear over Allen shaft at Botallack Mine can be seen in the background (2009)

14,000 tons of back tin, 20,000 tons of 12% copper ore and 1500 tons of arsenic.

The upper engine house is that of Pearce's whim, an all-enclosed 24-inch rotative engine similar to that preserved at Levant. From 1862 until 1875, this engine hoisted a skip on rails by way of a timber trestle from Boscawen diagonal shaft, the portal of which can be seen in the cliff face across the cove. The engine was almost certainly moved here a short distance from Wheal Button at the end of the headland, where it had been used to sink Boscawen shaft from 1858 to 1862 and where the footings of its house can still be seen. It was down this inclined shaft that the Prince and Princess of Wales (later King Edward VII and Queen Alexandra) descended in 1865, despite the fact that 8 men and a boy had been killed just two years earlier when the winding chain broke. Inside the house is a well-preserved cylinder bedstone, condenser pit and flywheel slot. The masonry outside supported the reduction gear and winding drum. The obvious extension to these loadings was probably made when the winding chain was replaced by wire rope following the 1863 tragedy. For lack of space, the house for the engine's single boiler is arranged behind and at an angle to the engine house. The flue (capped with granite slabs) runs steeply up the cliff to the remaining base of the stack. The hole for the steam inlet on the side of the rear (SW) wall furthest from the boiler house is an indication that the engine came from elsewhere. Both engine houses were consolidated by the Carn Brea Mining Society in 1984-85 (see also page 34).

9. WHEAL OWLES

On the cliffs to the south of Botallack Mine stand the remains of three engine houses. These were part of Wheal Owles, an old mine that is known to have been at work before 1725, but which reached its heyday in the 1860s when it produced significant quantities of both tin and copper. At that time it comprised an amalgamation of several older mines between the coast and Tregeseal (including Wheals Edward, Drea, Grouse, Boys and Cargodna) and had 11 steam engines at work. Its prosperity, however, was relatively short lived and most of the inland section (where three further engine houses survive) closed in the 1870s as metal prices fell. Several of the mine's principal shafts were by that time 190 fathoms (347m) deep. Output exceeded 8,500 tons of black tin and 2000 tons of copper ore.

Cargodna Pumping Engine (SW363329)

Standing prominently at the top of the cliff is the consolidated house of the 36-inch pumping engine of the Cargodna (or West Wheal Owles) section of the mine where all mining efforts were focused after 1884. The house contains the cylinder bedstone and had a single boiler positioned alongside the NE wall. Adjacent to the shaft (covered with a grating) are the footings for the balance box, which angle away from the house to the SW. It was on this section of the mine on the 10th January 1893 that miners working on the 65-fathom (119m) level (below adit) of Cargodna shaft (on the cliff edge to the west) inadvertently broke through to the flooded 148-fathom (271m) level (below surface) of Wheal Drea,

inundating the lower levels and closing the mine for good. Nineteen men and a boy were drowned and their bodies never recovered.

Cargodna Whim (SW362328)

The walling and foundations above the track SW of Cargodna Engine shaft mark the site of a 24-inch whim purchased secondhand from Wheal Cunning in 1882 to hoist twin skips in Cargodna shaft

Walling of the Cargodna 24-inch whim with Cargodna 36-inch pumping engine house to right and Botallack Mine in the background (above in 1967), and with Wheal Edwards 28-inch stamps to right (below in 2009)

Engine house of the 28-inch stamps at Wheal Edward (before and after consolidation) with Botallack Mine in the background (1967 and 2009).

arched opening in a front wall of normal thickness. The slotted, grease-smeared bedstone amid the masonry in front of the house is the footstep mounting of the winding drum, which had an upright rather than a horizontal axle so that it could hoist from any direction.

Wheal Edward stamps (SW362328)

On the opposite side of the track nearer the cliffs is the house of the 28-inch stamps engine of Wheal Edward erected in about 1870. Prior to the purchase of the whim, this multipurpose rotative engine served as the winding engine for Cargodna shaft and Wheal Edward incline shaft further south, as well as driving 16 heads of stamps on the landward side of the crankshaft loading, which contains prominent slots for a pair of flywheels. The large square opening in the rear wall, which is thicker than the side walls,

some way down the cliff to the NW (the intervening burrow is contoured to accommodate the skip road). The site is a unique survivor in that the whim was a self-supported ("entablature") engine and so lacked a bob wall, having instead an

suggests the house was intended for an auxiliary "back bob" to draw water from a shaft at the rear. However, no such shaft was found when the house was consolidated by the National Trust. When the whim was set to work in 1882, the engine's winding function was eliminated and the number of stamps doubled to 32. The house contains the cylinder bedstone and an attached stack built inside the east corner. The boiler house for the engine's single boiler lay alongside to the south, set back from the bob wall. The circular depression ahead of the house marks the site of a 50ft (16m) diameter convex buddle (the largest in Cornwall) used to concentrate the ore.

Wheal Owles Pumping Engine (SW365326)

About half a kilometre SE of Cargodna stands the house of the 30-inch pumping engine at Wheal Owles Engine shaft. Much of west and rear walls of the house have fallen and the shaft, which reached a depth of 196 fathoms (348m), is filled. The boiler house for a single boiler lies on the NW side with the stump of the separate stack at its NE end.

Wheal Drea Multipurpose Engine (SW365323)

To the south, beside Kenidjack Farm, stands the prominent 26-inch pumping /winding engine house of Wheal Drea, which dates from about 1857 and wound from Greenland's shaft across the field to the NE. It was later utilized to pump by way of flat-rods (and probably also to hoist) from Wheal Drea shaft diagonally across the field to the south. The house contains the cylinder bedstone, a prominent flywheel slot and pit on the east side of the bob wall, and a well-

The 30-inch pumping engine house at Wheal Owles Engine shaft (above) and the 26-inch multipurpose engine house at Wheal Drea (left). The stacks in the background are those of the Botallack arsenic works (above) and the 36-inch pumping engine at Lower Boscean Mine (left) (2009).

preserved boiler house (for a single boiler) alongside the NW wall. Greenland's and Wheal Drea shafts reached depths of 160 fathoms (293m) and 150 fathoms (274m), respectively.

The engine houses of the Wheal Drea 26-inch multipurpose engine (left), and the bob wall of the 30-inch stamps engine and base of the 40-inch pumping engine house at Wheal Grouse (below) (1965).

Wheal Grouse Stamps (SW369321)

To the SE of Wheal Drea, just west of the main road (B3306) on the hill approaching Tregeseal, stands the heavily overgrown bob wall of the 30-inch stamps engine house of Wheal Grouse at the eastern end of the Wheal Owles sett. Adjacent to the north is the now entirely overgrown base of the mine's 40-inch pumping engine, which had previously worked the Wherry Mine in Penzance.

10. BOSWEDDEN MINE (SW356323)

West of Wheal Drea, at the mouth of the Kenidjack (Nancherrow) valley, lie the scant consolidated remains of the 28-inch stamps engine house of Boswedden Mine. Another ancient mine (although records date only to 1782), Boswedden and Wheal Castle was formed as an amalgamation of several small tin and copper mines (including Wheal Call) in 1836. As Wheal Cunning United, the mine was expanded in 1872 to include Wheal Cunning to the south and Boscean up the valley, but was never very profitable and closed soon thereafter. Much of the remaining surface equipment was destroyed in a flash flood in 1892. Although the house was partly demolished during an army exercise in World War II, the engine's function can clearly be seen with pits at the foot of the bob wall for a pair of flywheels. The house of the engine's single boiler lay on the east side perpendicular to the engine house.

On the far side of the stream, beyond the crankshaft loading, is a cylinder bedstone and the granite mounting blocks for a balance box. These are all that remain of the house (also destroyed by the military) of the 37-inch pumping engine on Wheal Call Engine shaft. Flat rods from the balance box extended downstream to the prominent dressed granite wheel pit that also pumped this shaft (together with Praze shaft to the SW), the engine being used only during periods of prolonged dry weather when the stream level was low. The wheel pit was originally built for a 30ft (9.1m) wheel, but was enlarged around 1865 to

accommodate one with a diameter of 52ft (15.8m). Wheal Call Engine shaft was 85 fathoms (155m) deep. Further upstream are the extensive remains of the Kenidjack arsenic works, which include a furnace and numerous waterwheel-driven crushing mills.

Consolidated remains of the 28-inch stamps engine house at Boswedden Mine with the loading for the balance bob at Wheal Call Engine shaft in the floor of the valley below (2009).

View down the line of flat rods from Wheal Call Engine shaft through a tunnel in the burrows to the granite-walled pit of the 52 ft water wheel that drove them. The loading in the foreground is that of the balance bob (2009).

The spectacularly positioned pumping engine houses at Trewavas Mine, near Porthleven, prior their conservation in 2009 (2000).

CHAPTER 4 Marazion – Tregonning Mining District

The Marazion-Tregonning mining district occupies a triangular area between Marazion, Porthleven and Leedstown, and encircles the Tregonning-Godolphin granite, which underlies both of these hills and reaches the coast between Rinsey Head and Megiliggar Rocks. The district is an ancient one with many claims to fame. It was the first in Cornwall to use blasting (at Great Work in 1689), the first to erect a beam engine (at Wheal Vor in 1710), and the first to exploit china clay (at Wheal Grey in 1746). Wheal Vor was also the site (in 1835) of the county's first Brunton calciner (a circular, rotating furnace used to drive off impurities from ore minerals). An important producer of both copper and tin from the 16th century, the mining district's mineral wealth provided the financial underpinning of the great mining estates of Godolphin and Clowance, and several of its mines, most notably Great Work, Wheal Vor and Wheal Fortune, were long-lived and highly productive. Indeed, the output from Wheal Vor was large enough to warrant the building of its own smelting house in 1816. Mining exploited both NE- and WNW-trending lodes, those within and around the granite being mostly tin producers, whereas those to the north and west were early producers of copper.

Existing engine houses within the district are relatively few and widely scattered. However, many are of exceptional interest and those at Wheal Trewavas rank amongst the most dramatically sited in the whole of Cornwall. Although most are close to roads, not all are easily accessed and permission is required to visit those on private property.

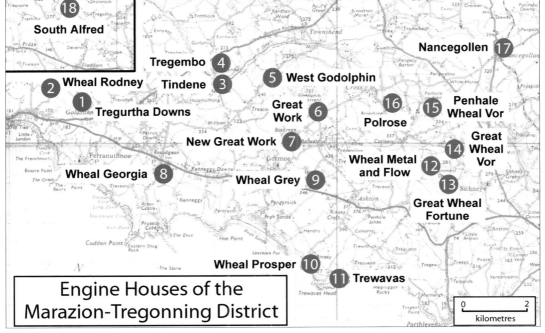

Engine Houses of the Marazion-Tregonning District

Two views of St. Aubyn's 80-inch pumping engine at Tregurtha Downs Mine before (above) and after (below) its conversion to a dwelling (1967 and 2010).

1. TREGURTHA DOWNS MINE (SW538310)

Beside Gears Lane to the NE of Goldsithney stands the imposing engine house (Listed Grade II and now converted into a remarkable dwelling) of St. Aubyn's 80-inch pumping engine better known as Robinson's engine – the name it acquired after its removal in 1903 to South Crofty Mine in Pool, where it is preserved. The engine was built in 1854 by Sandys, Vivian and Co. at the Copperhouse Foundry in Hayle to the design of Samuel Grose and had previously worked on Davey's shaft at Alfred Consols near Hayle until 1864, and as Pelly's engine at Crenver and Wheal Abraham near Crowan until 1876 when the pump rod broke and caused the piston to smash the cylinder. Purchased by Harvey and Co. of Hayle in 1882 and equipped with a new cylinder, piston, cylinder cap and piston rod, the engine was set to work at St. Aubyn's shaft at Tregurtha Downs on May 27th 1883. The engine survived a fire that gutted the engine house in 1889, and is said to have been worked at 13 strokes per minute in wet weather – very fast for so large an engine.

A productive but wet copper mine in the middle of the 18th century, Tregurtha Downs was worked only briefly (1831-40) as part of Marazion Mines in the 19th century prior to its reopening as a tin mine in 1883. Despite a productive start, the venture did not prove successful and the mine closed in 1895 by which time it was 95 fathoms (174m) deep. Briefly restarted during an 1899-1901 reworking of the mine, the pumping engine was sold to South Crofty in 1902. The unusual architectural style of the engine house suggests the work of a designer and is shared with those at East Wheal Rose and formerly at Wheal Agar, which also held large engines and were built at about the same time. The boiler house for the engine's four 12-ton boilers has been removed but lay to the south between the engine house and its separate stack (also Listed Grade II). The stack to the north (SW537312) served a horizontal stamps engine.

2. WHEAL RODNEY (WHEAL HAMPTON)
(SW531314)

To the NE of Tregurtha Downs, on the other side of Plain an Gwarry Lane, stands the unusual engine house of Wheal Rodney, which was converted into an equally unusual dwelling in 1999. The house shows architectural similarities to that at Tregurtha Downs and was erected (but never completed) at Wheal Rodney Engine shaft in 1913 as part of an unsuccessful attempt to work both mines for tin under the name of Wheal Hampton (1903-14). The engine, an 80-inch pumping engine built in 1864 by Bracewell and Griffiths of Burnley for the Trelogan lead mine on the North Wales coast, was delivered to the site but never erected. Plans of the engine include a decorative cast iron lintel for the plug door, which can still be seen. As Wheal Rodney, the mine had been an important copper producer in the 18th century and was successfully reworked for copper in the 19th century as part of Marazion Mines (1824-48) and Prosper United (1862-72).

Two views of the never-completed 80-inch pumping engine house at Wheal Rodney before (above) and after (below) its conversion to a dwelling (1967 and 2009).

The house of the 65-inch pumping engine at Tindene Mine (2009).

3. TINDENE MINE (SW572315)

Hidden in swampy woodlands beside the Hayle River at Retallack lies the well-preserved house (Listed Grade II) of the 65-inch pumping engine at Tindene Mine, which was set to work on Newton's Engine shaft in 1887 by engineer William Bennetts of Camborne. The engine had been purchased secondhand from Deer-park Mine on the Great Perran Iron Lode, near Perranporth, and was originally a 60-inch engine built by Perran Foundry that was later rebuilt as a 65-inch without a steam jacket. The sett was at work for copper as Retallack Mine in the 18th century and later as Halamanning (1851-58) and West Great Work (1862-76), but was reopened as Tindene and worked entirely for tin from 1886 until 1893. The engine house contains a fine cylinder bedstone of dressed granite. Massive granite loadings for the balance box lie at right angles to the house on the east side of the water-filled shaft, which still contains the pump rod. The boiler house for the engine's two boilers lay alongside to the west. The engine itself was finally dismantled in 1910 and moved to Wheal Kitty in St. Agnes where it worked at Sara's shaft until the mine closed in 1930. Its house at Wheal Kitty was restored in 2006 as the centrepiece of a small industrial estate. Newton's Engine shaft reached a depth of 29 fathoms (53m).

4. TREGEMBO MINE (SW570319)

At Tregembo, in the fields east of Relubbas, two chimneys – that of a 24-inch horizontal winding and pneumatic stamps engine (at SW571319) and that of a calciner (at SW572320) – are all that remain of this small tin mine, the main working periods of which (1880-84 and 1886-89) were entirely unsuccessful. But until its partial collapse and removal for safety reasons in 1986-87, it was also the site of a 60-inch pumping engine house (complete with some of its wooden window frames) erected on Engine or Tregembo shaft in 1882. The shaft was 58 fathoms (106m) deep when the engine was sold to Harvey and Co. of Hayle in 1889.

5. WEST GODOLPHIN MINE (SW584316)

Standing prominently on the western slope of Godolphin Hill to the east of Tindene is the well-preserved house and decorative stack (Listed Grade II) of West Godolphin Mine. This housed Wilson's 60-inch pumping engine purchased second-hand in April 1877 from Great Wheal Vor and erected using granite from an engine house at Bosence Mine across the valley to the north. At Great Wheal Vor the

Two views of the 60-inch pumping engine house at Tregembo Mine before its partial collapse and removal in 1986-87. Note the survival of a wooden frame in the middle chamber window of the rear wall (left) (1966).

engine had worked on Edward's shaft in the mine's Wheal Metal section where, in all likelihood, it was the same 60-inch engine erected on Ivey's shaft in 1859. The engine's boiler house stood on the same side as the stack. At work in the

The house of the 60-inch pumping engine at West Godolphin Mine (2009).

1830s, West Godolphin was a long-lived but relatively unproductive tin and copper mine known locally as "Wheal Junket". It was restarted in1859 as North Great Work, changed its name to Godolphin Hill in 1864 and became West Godolphin once again in 1866. The mine was 125 fathoms (229m) deep when it closed in 1889. Below the road, a solitary stack at SW579320 marks the site of the 15-inch stamps engine erected in 1876. The stack of the calciner (at SW578320) was struck by lightning in 1999.

6. GREAT WORK MINE (SW595308)

In the saddle between the Godolphin and Tregonning hills is the prominent house and distinctive telescope stack (both Listed Grade II) of the 60-inch pumping engine at Great Work Mine. The engine was built by Harvey and Co. of Hayle and erected on Leeds' shaft in 1835 where it continued to work (with a major overhaul in the 1860s) until the mine closed. Exploiting NE-trending lodes within the Godolphin-Tregonning granite, this old and prosperous tin mine dates from the early 16th century and is thought to be the site where blasting was introduced into mining by Thomas Epsley in 1689. The mine closed in 1793, but was restarted in 1810 to become a major tin producer in the 19th century. Underground operations ceased in 1873, but surface work continued and production was ongoing through many unsuccessful attempts to restart the mine between 1888 and 1901. In the 20th century, the

mine was worked as part of South West Cornwall Mines (1907-12) and Wheal Reeth (1927-37), the latter finally closing in 1943. During the mine's last reworking, Leeds' shaft was enlarged to a depth of 160 fathoms (293m) below adit and an electric hoist installed, for which purpose the engine house was cut down and provided with a flat roof. The house was conserved in 2005 and is now part of the National Trust.

7. NEW GREAT WORK (TREBOLLANCE) MINE
(SW586303)

Just a kilometer SW of Great Work Mine, lie the remains of New Great Work or Trebollance Mine, a short-lived tin prospect worked between 1890 and 1895. These include the base and attached stack of a 23-inch rotative engine house erected around 1890. The mine closed below adit after 1894 due to flooding and was unsuccessfully reworked in 1906-10 as Lady Gwendolin Mine.

Two views of Leeds' 60-inch pumping engine house and its distinctive telescope stack at Great Work Mine before and after its consolidation (top left in 1966 and above in 2009).

The 23-inch rotative engine house at New Great Work (Trebollance) Mine, taken when part of the cylinder opening survived in the rear wall (1966).

The 45-inch pumping engine house at Wheal Georgia (1965).

this small mine was worked for tin and copper in 1872-74. The mine exploited two lodes, one of which (Georgia lode), developed from Georgia shaft to the west (SW556294), had been previously worked by Wheal Grylls (1856-66) prior to its merger with several adjacent mines to form Great Western Mines (1868-73). But Wheal Georgia was a separate company. Wheal Speedwell, with which the mine has also been confused, lay to the south on the cliffs at Kenneggy. Georgia shaft reached a depth of 66 fathoms (121m).

9. WHEAL GREY (SW595291)

Close to the now-flooded Wheal Grey clay pit near Ashton (where Cornwall's china clay was first exploited) stands the well-preserved engine house (Listed Grade II) of a 36-inch pumping engine erected in 1897-98 to drain the clay pit. Built as a stamps engine by Charlestown Foundry for Polgooth Mine near St. Austell, it continued to work the mine's burrows after major operations ceased there in 1856. In 1878, it was moved to Rockhill

Two views of the 36-inch pumping engine house at Wheal Grey taken in 1966 and 2009. Note rearward extension of the lean-to boiler house (left).

8. WHEAL GEORGIA (SW558293)

Standing alone on Rosudgeon Common are the remains of a 45-inch pumping engine house erected on Engine shaft at Wheal Georgia during the brief period

Mine near Bugle, where it was again worked as a stamps engine, and from there moved to Woodclose Mine near Sticker, where it was used for both stamping and pumping. Adapted to pumping only, it remained at Wheal Grey until scrapped in 1935. Two of the cylinder holding-down bolts are visible inside the house and the footings of a balance box angled slightly away from the house can be seen on the east side of the water-filled shaft. The house of the engine's two boilers is also well preserved on the east side, extending behind the engine house to the separate stack, which is fed by two flues. The building immediately behind the house is that of a small horizontal engine.

10. WHEAL PROSPER (SW594270)

At the top of the cliff above Rinsey Cove stands the 30-inch pumping engine house (Listed Grade II) of Wheal Prosper, which

was erected on Engine shaft in 1860. The engine also pumped from Leeds' shaft below the car park to the NW by way of flat rods. Belying its name, the mine was never successful and closed in 1866. Previously known as Wheal Rinsey (1836-37 and 1842-43) and Rinsey United (1853-56), the mine was worked for tin and a little copper close to the Tregonning-Godolphin granite, which is exposed a short distance to the east towards Trewavas Head. The engine house, which is rather dramatically built from local slate with granite quoins, was acquired by the National Trust in 1969 and con-solidated in 1970-71. Unfortunately, this

Two views of the 30-inch pumping engine at Wheal Prosper in 1966 (top) and 2010 (bottom), before and after consolidation in 1970-71. Damage to the cylinder opening and boiler house door visible prior to conservation (top) was probably sustained when the engine was removed.

The two cliff-edge pumping engine houses of Trewavas Mine on New Engine shaft (foreground) and Old Engine shaft (background) prior to their consolidation. Note the track of the tramway excavated in the cliff behind the house on Old Engine shaft (2000).

early attempt at conservation appears to have restored the boiler house door (below the steam inlet on the NW side) as a window, and has removed almost all traces of the house of the engine's single boiler, which stood alongside this wall. Doubtless for reasons of stability, the gracefully proportioned stack is attached to the opposite corner. The shaft (now filled) reached the 50-fathom (91m) level below adit at 20 fathoms (37m). The mouth of the shaft's large adit lies at the foot of the cliff below the engine house.

11. TREWAVAS MINE (SW600265)

Perched dramatically on the cliffs at Trewavas Head, the two engine houses (Listed Grade II) of Trewavas Mine rival those of Botallack Mine in their spectacular location (see page 50). This short-lived but productive copper mine lies at the southern margin of the Tregonning-Godolphin granite, the contact of which can be seen in the form of sheets of granite cutting darker country rock in the cliffs above Megiliggar Rocks to the east. The mine was worked between 1833-34 and 1846 when its workings beneath the sea were breached and the mine was flooded.

The two engine houses are those of pumping engines erected on Old Engine shaft in 1834 (SW599625) and, at slightly higher elevation to the east, on New Engine shaft in 1838 (SW601226). The former occupies a precarious site excavated into the cliff, the slot-like cylinder opening in the rear wall extending up to the second chamber in order to allow the cylinder and beam to be installed from the rear down the slope of the cliff. Little remains of the boiler house, which occupied a position on the south side of the engine house with a flue that can be traced to the base of the stack at the top of the cliff. But the boiler house door is clearly evident in the south wall of the engine house and traces of white limewash can be seen on the wall above the level of the boiler house roofline. Built out on made ground immediately south of the boiler house is one of the best preserved manual capstan platforms in Cornwall, its flat, circular surface today providing a ready-made site for cliff landing practice by helicopter pilots from RNAS Culdrose. The base of a stack just north of the engine house is possibly that of the mine's 18-inch steam whim. Because of its precipitous location, ore from the lode and coal for the engine were carried up and down the cliff by way of a horse-whim-operated tram road, evidence of which can still be seen.

The second house is that of a 45-inch engine built by Harvey and Co. of Hayle, which was sold in 1844 when it was replaced by a 70-inch engine erected on Diagonal shaft at the top of the cliff. By this time, the engine was also working Old Engine shaft by means of flat rods, the entrenched route of which can still be traced. The separate stack behind the house is unusual in its use of stone rather than brick above the medial corbelling. It served a boiler house on the SE side of the engine house. Of the 70-inch engine house nothing now remains, but Diagonal shaft reached a depth of 100 fathoms (183m) offshore.

Both engine houses were consolidated by the National Trust in 2009 following the Trust's acquisition of the mine site and 30 acres of the spectacular coastline of which it is part, in 2008.

Two views of the engine houses at Trewavas Mine taken in September 1967 and after consolidation in June 2010 (right), showing the slot-like cylinder opening in the house on Old Engine shaft in the foreground. In the background (right), pale granite sheets intruding the darker country rock can be seen in the cliffs at Megiliggar Rocks.

Two views of Watson's multipurpose 30-inch rotative engine house and separate decorative stack at Wheal Metal and Flow (2009 and 1967).

12. WHEAL METAL AND FLOW (SW623295)

On Carnmeal Downs NE of Breage is the engine house and separate stack (both Listed Grade II) of Wheal Metal and Flow. This housed Watson's 30-inch rotative stamping and pumping engine erected secondhand when the mine was started in 1885 to recover tin from the sandy waste deposits (or "flow") from neighbouring Wheal Vor and Wheal Metal. The stack (with ornamental brickwork) was connected via a shallow underground flue to the single boiler house on the south side of the engine house. The engine operated stamps, but also pumped from Watson's shaft at the rear of the building using an auxilliary "back bob" mounted on the rear wall at a slightly higher level than the main beam to allow for the linkage between the two. The shaft had been sunk to a depth of 47 fathoms (86m) earlier in the 19th century as part of West Wheal Metal and was used to provide water for the stamps and tin dressing floors. The engine ceased work in 1901.

13. GREAT WHEAL FORTUNE (SW625287)

South of Carnmeal Downs, at the SW end of the Conqueror openwork that marks the site of Wheal Fortune, stand the remains of the engine house and twin flywheel slots of a 33-inch stamps engine erected second-hand in 1872 when the tin mine was reworked as Great Wheal Fortune. The engine had been purchased through Harvey and Co., of Hayle from Bosworthen and Penzance Consols mine (SW412290), near Sancreed (where it had been advertised for sale in 1867 and where the base of its house survives), for the purpose of reworking the burrows and exploring at shallow depth. Having stood idle, it was

openwork mining dating to the beginning of the 16th century. It was most productive between 1855 and 1868 (when deep mining ceased), and was reworked again as New Fortune (1892-95), as part of Wheal Metal and Flow (to 1901), as the Breage Valley Mining Company (to 1905), and as New Great Wheal Fortune (1908-09).

14. GREAT WHEAL VOR (WHEAL METAL)
(SW629299)

Standing in private property beside the Carleen to Helston road is the finely proportioned house (Listed Grade II) of Ivey's 85-inch pumping engine. The engine was erected in 1864 on the Wheal Metal section of this rich and venerable tin mine to replace a 60-inch pumping

One of the twin flywheel pits and the surviving side walls, suggests the house was a multipurpose 33-inch engine house at Great Wheal Fortune as they appeared in 1995 (photo by Kenneth Brown).

refurbished in 1887 by a new company who installed a Lancashire boiler and 16 heads of stamps. A winding drum was also fitted at the end of the stamps axle for hauling up an incline from the openwork. The engine additionally pumped water for tin dressing from an adit shaft at the rear of the house (where there is evidence of a balance box) using an auxilliary "back bob" like Watson's engine at Wheal Metal and Flow. The boiler house and the base of the stack lie alongside to the south. Except for part of the north side wall, little survives of the house itself. The engine stopped work in about 1889 when the mine closed. As Wheal Fortune, the mine had enjoyed a long and prosperous history, with

Boiler house side (with steam inlet at rear) of Ivey's 85-inch pumping engine house on the Wheal Metal section of Great Wheal Vor (2010)

Two views of Ivey's 85-inch pumping engine house on the Wheal Metal section of Great Wheal Vor (1967 and 2010).

engine that stood on the north side of the shaft. The latter was probably re-erected on Edward's shaft across the road to the SW, from whence it was purchased in 1877 by West Godolphin Mine (where its engine house still stands). The 85-inch engine was built by Harvey and Co. of Hayle in 1855 and had previously worked at Trelawney's shaft on the Wheal Vor section of the mine near Carleen (SW622303). It is believed to have been transferred to Ivey's shaft together with its house. Around 1880, the engine was moved to the Wylam pumping station of the Newcastle and Gatehead Waterworks in Northumberland, where it survived into the 1940s. The engine's boiler house stood on the SE side with its steam inlet at the rear of the engine.

Wheal Vor, which dates to the 15th century, was the first mine in Cornwall to use a beam engine (a Newcomen engine erected in 1710) and, during its heyday (1812-48), the mine's peak productivity amounted to almost a third of Cornwall's total tin production. The mine had its own smelting works that, for some time, was producing 200 tons of metallic tin per month. In total, the mine is thought to have raised some 60,000 tons of black tin. However, the engine house dates from the first of three (1853-77, 1906-10 and 1967) largely unsuccessful attempts to rework the mine. Productivity during this first reworking amounted to some 9400 tons of black tin. Ivey's shaft reached its final depth of 227 fathoms (415m) in 1870.

15. PENHALE WHEAL VOR (SW622309)

Entirely concealed amid overgrowth at Penhale-an-drea, east of Godolphin Cross, are the remains of the house of a long-lived 40-inch pumping engine built by St. Austell Foundry in 1855. The engine was erected on Guiterrez's shaft at Penhale Wheal Vor in 1865 having been purchased from North Wheal Vor, the name under which the tin mine had operated between 1859 and 1862. Prior to this (as Penhale Mine), the mine had been part of Wheal Vor. Penhale Wheal Vor closed in 1873. In 1879, the engine was sold to St. Just United near Cape Cornwall where it worked with the cylinder linered down to 36-inches as Weston's engine (on Bayley's shaft) from 1880 until 1888. At St. Just United it was served by two boilers. In 1890 it was sold to Trethosa Clay Works near St. Stephen where it remained until scrapped in 1934. Much of the engine house has fallen, but the bob wall and one

Interior view of the 40-inch pumping engine house at Penhale Wheal Vor showing the bob wall and plug door (right), and the boiler house door and steam inlet (left) (2010).

side wall survive intact. The boiler house stood alongside to the SE. Guiterrez's shaft, which remains open, was 43 fathoms (79m) deep, but the mine reached a depth of 180 fathoms (329m). The mine was briefly reworked in 1886-89.

16. POLROSE MINE (SW613310)

On the grounds of Polrose Farm between Godolphin Cross and Carleen stands the picturesque house (Listed Grade II) of a 40-inch pumping engine erected on Engine shaft in 1877. At work for both tin and copper at the end of the 18th century and as part of Wheal Vor in the early 19th century, Polrose was worked briefly in 1840-44 and, as East Great Work, in 1863-67. Although never very productive, the main working periods of this mine

The picturesque 40-inch pumping engine house at Polrose Mine (2009).

were for tin in 1872-78 and 1880-84, by which time Engine shaft had reached a depth of 137 fathoms (251m). The opening for the steam inlet shows that the boiler house, of which there is little sign, lay on the SW side opposite the attached stack.

17. NANCEGOLLAN MINE (SW640324)

In Nancegollan, just north of the road to Porkellis, stand the engine house and graceful separate stack (both Listed Grade II) of Nancegollan Mine. The house is likely to be that of a 40-inch pumping engine offered for sale in 1873 having been worked for just a year. Under the names Nancegollan Mine (in the 1830s, 1850-53 and 1867-69), Pengelly Mine (in 1849 and 1857-59), Florence United (1872-73) and Great Wheal Worthy (1882-1884), this small tin mine was worked intermittently but unsuccessfully throughout the 19th century. It was worked again in 1907-14 and (for wolfram) in 1927-29, one of the adventurers on these occasions

Two vews of the engine house and separate stack of the 40-inch pumping engine at Nancegollan Mine from the front (2010) and from the boiler house side with openings in the side wall for the boiler house door, steam inlet and main girder (1967).

the shaft sunk 20 fathoms (37m) below adit. Known locally as "Wheal Drunk," this unsuccessful venture had been worked as Bandowers Mine prior to 1819, but the only recorded production is 3 tons of copper ore in 1866. Of the engine house, only the north wall (with openings for the boiler house door and steam inlet, and the base of an attached stack at its east end), and part of the bob wall remain standing. The engine had two boilers. Loadings for a balance box are discernible on the north side of the filled shaft.

being Herbert Hoover, the future President of the United States. The engine's boiler house stood alongside to the east. The depth of the engine shaft was 42 fathoms (77m).

18. SOUTH ALFRED (SW588362)
Of the thriving mining area once centered on Leedstown, little now remains. But standing alone in the fields north of Fraddam, SE of its far more important namesake, Wheal Alfred, is the ruinous engine house of South Alfred Mine. This housed a 45-inch pumping engine erected in 1861 when the mine was reopened and

North side wall and part of bob wall (left) of the 45-inch pumping engine house at South Alfred.

Engine house of the 40-inch pumping engine at Medlyn Moor Mine near Porkellis (2009)

CHAPTER 5 **Helston – Wendron Mining District**

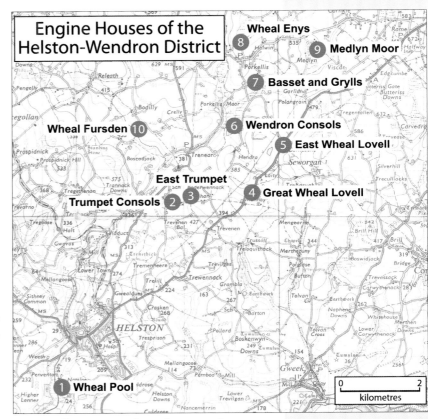

The small Helston-Wendron mining district runs NE from the Loe Valley to Carnkie between the River Cober and the main Helston-Falmouth road (A394). The district was largely a tin-producing area along the southern margin of the Carnmenellis granite, the boundary of which runs more-or-less E-W between Helson and Wendron. However, tin production, records of which date back to the 1580s, was mainly from the rich alluvial deposits of the Cober Valley, and the underground mines, which reached their heyday in the 1860s, were mostly shallow and small. Existing engine houses cluster around the villages of Porkellis and Wendron, the latter lying close to the Poldark Mine Heritage Complex in Trenear, which makes use of the old Wheal Roots workings of Wendron Consols and counts among its exhibits the 30-inch Cornish pumping engine at work at the Greensplat china clay pit near St. Austell until 1959. Although few in number, many of the engine houses have interesting features and all lie close to roads. However, not all are easily accessed and several are on private property and require permission to visit.

The 20-inch pumping engine house at Wheal Pool, possibly the oldest in Cornwall (2010).

1. WHEAL POOL (SW653263)

On the east side of Loe Valley, SW of Helston, the partially consolidated engine house at Wheal Pool is a contender for the oldest in Cornwall. This housed a 20-inch pumping engine of 1855, but there is evidence that it was briefly occupied during an earlier working of the mine around 1800 by a 30-inch Boulton and Watt pumping engine. Excavations have further revealed that it is likely to have been used before this for a 30/36-inch Hornblower and Winwood compound engine erected in 1794 – the fore-and-aft arrangement of the two cylinders of the latter engine accounting for the unusual shape of the house, which is long in relation to its width. Wheal Pool was a small silver-lead mine developed within the Mylor slates, well removed from the Carnmenellis granite. It is believed to have been at work well before its first recorded working in 1790 and was developed on a north-south lead lode that it exploited to a depth of 50 fathoms (92m).

2. TRUMPET CONSOLS

On the east side of the River Cober, SW of Wendron, two engine houses (both Listed Group II) mark the site of Trumpet Consols, an amalgamation of several setts that formed one of the district's most important tin mines between 1845 and 1877. Straddling the southern contact of

the Carnmenellis granite, the setts (including Old Trumpet and Wheals Ann, Noon, Dream and Valls) worked east-west lodes containing tin and some copper.

Wheal Ann Pumping Engine (SW678303)

On the east side of Rowe's Lane is the house of the 48-inch pumping engine at Wheal Ann. This engine house shows several unique features because the engine was of Watt-type with an indoor condenser and a wooden bob. The bob wall consequently lacks a plug door and is much thinner than those needed to support a cast iron bob, particularly towards the top. The position of the main girder opening close to the rear wall (giving no room to set the cylinder cover during heavy maintenance) is also indicative of an early engine. Some footings and the opening for the steam inlet show the boiler house to have been

on the NE side. The small angled opening at the base of the bob wall circulated cooling water for the condenser. The engine was offered for sale in June 1848 and the house has lain empty since about 1850 when the engine was moved a quarter mile SW to the Wheal Valls part of the group. It was offered for sale in August 1877 but remained at Wheal Valls until dismantled in1889. The ultimate depth of Wheal Ann was 142 fathoms (260m).

Winding Engine House (SW675303)

The prominent winding engine house between Rowe's Lane and the main Helston-Wendron road (B3297) is likely to be that of a 30-inch winding engine that served Wheal Dream, the deepest sett of the group at 210 fathoms (384m), a quarter of a mile to the west. The

Wheal Ann 48-inch pumping engine house at Trumpet Consols (2009).

Wheal Ann 48-inch pumping engine house as it looked in 1967, prior to the destruction of the separate stack by lightning in the 1980's.

Two views of the 30-inch winding engine house at Trumpet Consols showing the loadings ahead of the bob wall for the crankshaft, flywheel and winding drum (1967 and 2009).

Base of the 30-inch pumping engine house at East Trumpet Mine (2009).

prominent loadings are those of the flywheel and crankshaft. Like that at Wheal Ann, the house suggests an engine of early design with an indoor condenser and valve gear operated by plug rods from the bob rather than by eccentrics driven off the crankshaft. The base of the boiler house wall and steam inlet opening on the SE side place the boiler house (with a single boiler) on this side of the building.

3. EAST TRUMPET MINE (SW679304)

Amid the burrows in the field to the NE of Wheal Ann is the heavily overgrown base of the engine house at East Trumpet Mine. The house is that of a 30-inch pumping engine that dates from this largely unproductive tin mine's short and spirited working life between 1867 and 1871.

During this time the engine shaft was sunk to 82 fathoms (150m) and the whim shaft (some 100m to the west) to 105 fathoms (192m). Footings for the balance box lie on the north side of the filled engine shaft.

4. GREAT WHEAL LOVELL (SW704304)

On the east side of the main Helston-Falmouth road (A394) at Manhay, two chimney stacks mark the site of Great Wheal Lovell, a rich but short-lived tin mine active in the 1860s. The older (shorter) stack to the NE is of unknown function, but the larger one served the boiler house of Cape's 50-inch pumping engine. Cape's engine house, which stood to the SE, was a prominent roadside landmark until the A394 was widened in the 1980s. The engine's two boilers also served a 16-inch horizontal winding engine that stood in the field close by.

On the other side of the A394, in the private grounds of Trelowareth Farm, is the ivy-covered ruin of the mine's only surviving engine house (SW703305). This housed a 28-inch stamps engine that is said to have been single-acting. If so, a heavy weight, either on the connecting rod or the outdoor end of the bob, would have been needed to return the piston to

Bob wall and separate stack of Cape's 50-inch pumping engine house at Great Wheal Lovell as they appeared prior to the loss of the bob wall when the neighbouring A394 (to right) was widened (1967).

the top of the cylinder following the power stroke. An opening for the steam inlet in the rear wall suggests the boiler house was built across the back of the house with the stack partially built into the NE corner.

5. EAST WHEAL LOVELL (SW670315)

On the west side of the A394 at Carnebone stands the prominent engine house (Listed Grade II) of East Wheal Lovell. This housed Rogers' 50-inch pumping engine erected on the Tregonebris section of this once celebrated tin mine in 1869 and worked until 1881, the last to do so in the district. Until 1867, the engine had worked at Great East Lovell, a short-

Two views of the 28-inch stamps engine house at Great Wheal Lovell. Note (top) the steam inlet in the rear wall and the stack built partially into the NE comer of the house (1967 and 2009).

lived venture three quarters of a mile to the NE, where it was erected new in 1864. The engine house is unusual in having only two floors, so that the driver's floor was well above the cylinder bed. As a result, the plug door and cylinder opening are positioned high in their respective walls. A deep recess at the front of the cylinder bed (with holes for five holding down bolts rather than the usual four) also suggests that the exhaust port emerged from beneath the cylinder and, hence, the exhaust valve was low down, accounting for the unusually low position of the eduction opening to the condenser at the base of the bob wall. The engine's

boiler house stood on the SW side (where its roofline can still be seen well above the existing lean-to barn) and the stack is built against the rear wall rather than at the corner. Loadings for the balance box lie on the SW side of the filled shaft, which had been sunk to a depth of about 100 fathoms (183m) by the time the mine closed.

Two views of Rogers' 50-inch pumping engine house at East Wheal Lovell showing (right) the high cylinder opening, the roofline of the boiler house just above the boiler house door in the SW side wall, and the stack offset from the west corner of the building (2009).

(above) Heavily overgrown corner of the bob wall (centre) and water-filled shaft (bottom left) of the 70-inch pumping engine house at Wendron Consols (2009).

worked several lines of flat rods. An old alluvial tin mine that records show had a stamping mill as early as 1493, Wendron Consols was reopened as an underground mine in 1852. It productively worked at least six east-west lodes containing tin and a little copper until 1869, by which time it had reached a depth of 100 fathoms (183m). The 70-inch engine was erected in 1855 and advertised for sale in September 1866.

7. BASSET AND GRYLLS MINE (SW693 329)
Hidden amid woodlands in Lower Porkellis is the well-preserved consolidated engine house of Basset and Grylls. This housed a 60-inch pumping engine erected on Tyacke's Shaft in 1860 following the tragic flooding of an older section of the mine (then known as

6. WENDRON CONSOLS (SW689 319)
In marshy woodlands NE of Trenear, the water-filled Engine shaft and heavily overgrown base of the bob wall are all that remain of this important tin mine's 70-inch pumping engine, which also

(below) Two views of the 60-inch pumping engine house at Basset and Grylls before and after its consolidation (1967 and 2009). Openings in the side wall (left) are for the boiler house door, steam inlet, drain and main girder.

Porkellis United) in August 1858 when a run of ground entombed six men and a boy. Openings for a door, steam inlet and drain place the boiler house on the east side, opposite to that of the attached stack. As Porkellis United and later, as Basset and Grylls, the mine was one of the oldest and richest in the district with workings for alluvial tin on Porkellis Moor, where mining activity was centred, dating back to at least 1574. Developed on a network of east-west lodes beneath the moor, underground mining is believed to have started in 1845 and continued until 1880, only to be restarted in 1907 and again in the 1920's and 30's. Tyacke's shaft, a less productive offshoot of this activity, was sunk to 80 fathoms (146m). The site of the mine's most recent working is marked by dressing floors and a chimney on the edge of Porkellis Moor, a quarter of a mile to the ESE (SW689328).

8. WHEAL ENYS (SW690 336)

A short distance NE of Porkellis Bridge stands the engine house (Listed Grade II) of Wheal Enys, which was tastefully converted into a dwelling in the 1990s.

The 24-inch stamps engine house at Wheal Enys in 2009 (below), following its conversion to a dwelling and in 1967 (above), following an earlier attempt to convert the building to a dwelling by creating door and window openings in its south wall.

Two views of the 40-inch pumping engine house at Medlyn Moor Mine before (left in 1967) and after (right in 2009) a non-specialist effort to consolidate the rear and south walls so that the building could be used as a hay barn, resulting in an enlarged middle chamber window and main girder opening.

This housed a 24-inch stamps engine built by the Copperhouse Foundry of Sandys, Vivian and Co. and erected in 1852 following the start of underground mining in 1849. The engine worked 32 heads of stamps. The boiler house (now part of the dwelling) stands alongside to the north. Although productive for tin on a small scale, the mine was never profitable and, following its closure, the engine was offered for sale in April 1860.

9. MEDLYN MOOR MINE (SW707336)

Near Medlyn, between Porkellis and Carnkie, is the engine house (Listed Grade II) of Medlyn Moor Mine. This held a 40-inch pumping engine erected in 1873 during a later working of this tin mine (the mine was earlier worked with a 30-inch engine between 1846 and 1854). Both workings were attempts to exploit underground what had previously been an important alluvial tin streaming ground, but falling metal prices forced the mine to close in 1879 when the engine was sold off. Openings for a door and steam inlet place the boiler house on the north side (see page 68) and, as at East Wheal Lovell, the stack is built against the rear wall rather than at the corner. Loadings for a balance box lie on the south side of the grassed over shaft, which had reached 33 fathoms (60m) in 1873.

10. WHEAL FURSDEN (SW669318)

On the west side of the valley at Bodilly Mill, NW of Wendron, is the overgrown base of the diminutive 17-inch pumping engine house of Wheal Fursden. This unsuccessful tin mine closed in 1860 having been described earlier the same year as a young venture worked to a depth of only 20 fathoms (37m) below adit. The shaft remains open. The engine was offered for sale in 1862.

Diminutive 17-inch pumping engine house of Wheal Fursden with base of bob wall and open shaft to right (2010).

The engine houses of Wheal Coates (from left to right, Towanroath 36-inch pumping engine, multipurpose 24-inch stamps and whim, and all-enclosed 18-inch winding engine) viewed north from Chapel Porth (2010).

CHAPTER 6 **Porthtowan – St. Agnes Mining District**

The Porthtowan-St. Agnes mining district hugs the north coast of Cornwall between Porthtowan beach and Trevaunance Cove. The northern half of the district, north of Chapel Porth, was a rich tin-producing area centred on St. Agnes and exploited a set of NE-trending mineral veins, most of which dip to the NW. In this area, the slates that make up the district's bedrock lie close to the underlying granite, which is exposed in two small bodies on St. Agnes Beacon and at Cligga Head. Southward from Chapel Porth to Porthtowan, however, the mineral veins typically dip SE and the mines were copper producers. The district preserves a long history of visible mining activity. Evidence of early mining can be seen in the ancient workings that riddle the cliffs above Trevaunance Cove, and activity did not cease until the closure of Polberro Mine in 1941, brought on by World War II. Although the engine houses that symbolize this important mining district are now few, most are readily accessible and included among their number are those of Wheal Coates (one of the best known Cornish mine sites) and Wheal Kitty, where the entire mine complex has been restored as office and workshop space. In nearby Trevellas Combe, the district also includes Blue

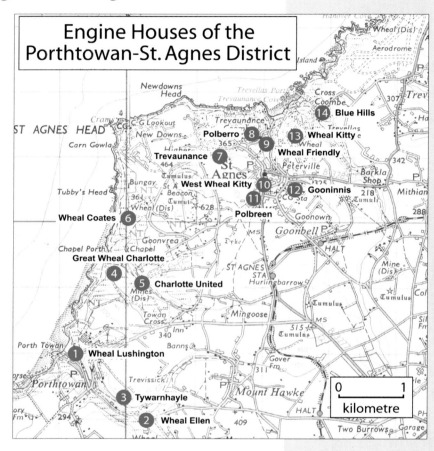

Hills Tin, where a set of waterwheel-driven Cornish stamps and a small-scale ore dressing floor has been restored to working order as a tourist attraction.

The all-enclosed rotative engine house at Wheal Lushington converted into a dwelling (1967 and 2010).

Wheal Ellen pumping engine house with that of John's 70-inch pumping engine at Tywarnhayle on the skyline (1967).

1. WHEAL LUSHINGTON (SW691479)

At the foot of the cliff at Porthtowan beach stands a well-preserved engine house (Listed Grade II) formerly used as a café and now converted to a dwelling. The house dates from a planned reworking of Wheal Lushington (or West Wheal Towan) in 1872, under the name of New Wheal Towan, and was intended for an all-enclosed rotative pumping engine that was bought secondhand from Ireland but never installed. Instead, it was left to rust outside when the venture ran out of capital. The engine was intended to pump the old workings to the SW by running flat rods down an adit (now-blocked) immediately behind the house. Loadings for the crankshaft and gearing can be seen on the seaward side of the house. The location of the cockpit (now the basement) indicates that the engine was to have faced NE with the flywheel indoors. The boiler house (if built) would have lain alongside the SW wall, to which the truncated stack is attached. The missing bricks from the stack were used to form the foundation of the bungalow next door, which was formerly the wooden count house of Wheal Charlotte up-valley from Charlotte United. Wheal Lushington comprised a number of small setts on the cliffs to the south that date to the early 1800s and produced minor amounts of tin, copper, lead and zinc from workings no more than 50 fathoms (91m) deep. Records for West Towan show 550 tons of black tin raised between 1852 and 1858.

2. WHEAL ELLEN (SW702469)

At the head of the deep valley that carries the Porthtowan stream stands a fine pumping engine house (Listed Grade II) with an unusual castellated stack. This

Another view of the Wheal Ellen 70-inch pumping engine house with the house of John's 70-inch pumping engine at Tywarnhayle on the skyline (2010).

engine house was commissioned by a Manchester-based firm in 1866 for a 70-inch engine then standing idle at Boscawen Mine, near Blackwater. However, as with the house at Wheal Lushington, the engine was never installed and the venture (the Ellen United Copper and Zinc Mining Co.) wound up the following year. The builders were never paid and the 70-inch engine later went to Blencowe Consols, near St. Stephen, and ended up at Van Mine in central Wales. The boiler house is gone but lay alongside the east wall. Prior to this unsuccessful enterprise, Wheal Ellen produced over 9,000 tons of copper in the period 1845-61. A brief attempt to reopen the mine in 1907 (the concrete ruins of which lie a short distance east of the engine house) was also unsuccessful.

3. TYWARNHAYLE (UNITED HILLS) MINE

Occupying the NE side of the steep Porthtowan valley, Tywarnhayle was the name given to a combined group of copper mines, one of which (Wheal Rock) dates from at least 1750. Renamed United Hills in 1809 (a name it retained until 1847), it closed in 1815 only to be reopened in 1826. Soon after, in 1827 and 1830, the

Two views of John's 70-inch pumping engine at Tywarnhayle (United Hills) Mine (2010).

mine suffered two boiler explosions, the latter causing nine fatalities. The mine was most prosperous in the late 1830s, and from 1826 until its closure in 1852, produced more than 75,000 tons of copper ore as well as minor amounts of lead. In 1849, the mine incorporated South Wheal Towan, a lone chimney of which (possibly that of a 70-inch pumping engine offered for sale in 1847) can be seen at Echo Corner, at the junction with the St. Agnes-Portreath road (SW696475). The mine was unsuccessfully reopened as Tywarnhayle between 1859 and 1864, and again in 1906-07, when an electrically driven centrifugal pump (the first to be used in Cornwall) was installed in Taylor's shaft, the power house for which stands close to the road (SW698472). The endeavour also employed an Elmore vacuum flotation plant for treating low-grade copper ore, and the concrete and masonry ruins of this (the world's first commercial froth flotation plant) can be seen some 300m further up the road on the left hand side (SW701471).

John's Pumping Engine (SW700472)

Perched high on the hillside overlooking the head of the valley is the magnificently sited house (Listed Grade II) of a 70-inch pumping engine erected secondhand at John's shaft in 1861. Built by the St. Austell Foundry in 1853, the engine had an unusually long indoor stoke of 12 feet, and had previously worked at Great Hewas tin mine near St. Austell. When Tywarnhayle closed in 1864, it was moved to Hind's shaft at Wheal Uny, where its house still stands. A prominent feature of John's engine house, doubtless necessitated by its exposed position, is the walled enclosure for the balance box on the far side of the filled shaft (see page 16). The stone plinth beside the shaft supported one of the shear legs, the round capstan plat and winding drum pit for which can be made out on the NE side. The house of the engine's three boilers lay alongside to the NE, the flue hole for which is visible at the base of the attached stack. John's shaft reached the 80-fathom (146m) level. Below the engine house and some distance to the ESE is the lone decapitated stack of the mine's crusher engine (SW703473).

Taylor's Pumping Engine (SW698472)

Built into the cliff on the lower slope of the valley beside Taylor's shaft (with the cockpit cut into the bedrock) is an engine house (Listed Grade II) of particular interest in that the 58-inch pumping engine it housed had a wooden bob and is said to have been the last such engine in Cornwall. It is believed to have come from Lambo Mine in Gwinear and was first erected at an unknown location in 1826 before being moved to Taylor's shaft. The engine also pumped from James' shaft, high on the valley side some 380 metres to the east (SW702473), by flat rods that were attached to the main bob through the opening high in the rear wall. The engine ceased work when the mine closed in 1852, but stood idle at the site for many years thereafter. The house is unusual in that the sides of the bob wall extend to roof level (perhaps to stabilize the wing walls), and the bob opening is merely a

slot large enough to accommodate the bob and the balance box-like kingpost and bridle truss used to strengthen it. With no access from the rear, the enlarged plug door would have served as the cylinder opening through which the engine parts were taken into the house. Traces of the site of the balance box can be seen on the SE side of the shaft. The site of the boiler house between the engine house and separate stack (which has a square base) was occupied by an electric hoist during the 1906-07 reworking, the concrete foundations of which can still be seen. It was also at Taylor's shaft that a submersible electric pump (built by Worthington and Co.) was first used in Cornwall in 1906. The shaft, which is capped with a steel grating, reached a depth of 87 fathoms (159m).

Taylor's 58-inch pumping engine house at Tywarnhayle (United Hills) Mine (2010).

The bob wall of the 60-inch pumping engine house at Great Wheal Charlotte (2010).

4. GREAT WHEAL CHARLOTTE (SW697491)

Standing high on the hill overlooking Chapel Porth, the lone bob wall (Listed Grade II) of the house of a 60-inch pumping engine put up for auction in 1842 is all that now stands of this once important copper mine. Opened or reopened around 1820, the mine initially exploited rich copper deposits at shallow depths. The 60-inch engine may have been first erected at the mine in 1828 when an earlier 38-inch engine was offered for sale so that it could be replaced with a larger one. Its erection at Engine shaft, however, dates from the mine's final working, which ended in 1840. The shaft, now filled, was sunk to the main lode (visible in the cliff at low tide from the beach below) at a depth of 132 fathoms (241m). Surviving output records of 2,800 tons of copper ore in 1834-36 and 1840 are unlikely to be representative of the mine's productivity. The site was bought by the National Trust in 1956.

5. CHARLOTTE UNITED (SW701490)

A little over half a kilometer up the valley from the Chapel Porth car park, beyond the tin streaming site on the north bank known as Old Century Tin Works, stands the house (Listed Grade II) of a 36-inch pumping engine erected in 1869-70 on

Engine shaft, the adit for which can be seen beside the footpath below. The engine is said to have been moved to this short-lived copper mine (then called New Wheal Charlotte) from Wheal Freedom (across the valley to the north near the roadside cluster of houses), where it was at work by 1854. It was put up for sale in 1873 and again in 1878, just a year after the mine was renamed Charlotte United. It was subsequently re-erected at Polbreen's North shaft in St. Agnes, during a short-lived attempt to rework the mine as New Polbreen in the 1880s. Despite National Trust ownership, the engine house has not been consolidated and consists of only two walls and an attached stack. On the far side of the open shaft, but not quite in line with the house, is the overgrown pit of the balance box. The house of the engine's single boiler lay alongside the remaining (north) wall.

6. WHEAL COATES

On the cliffs north of Chapel Porth (see page 80), the three beam engine houses at Wheal Coates occupy one of the most picturesque settings of any mine in Cornwall. Mining activity here goes back

several centuries (the earliest documentary record dating to 1692), and evidence of ancient workings can be seen in the form of narrow open-works north of the engine houses and in the cliff below them. The mine itself was in operation in 1802 and, although generally unsuccessful, it was worked intermittently, largely for tin but earlier for copper, until 1889. However, the main period of activity occurred in the decade following 1872, when underground activity started in earnest, after which deep underground mining ceased although the engines were left in situ. The mine was briefly re-worked in 1911-14 when horizontal pumping and winding engines were installed, along with a set of stamps driven by a gas engine. The site is in the care of the National Trust.

Two views of the 36-inch pumping engine house at Charlotte United (1967 and 2010).

Two views of the house of the 24-inch dual-purpose stamps and winding engine at Wheal Coates with the engine houses and separate stack of the all-enclosed 18-inch whim and horizontal winder behind (2010).

Dual-purpose stamps and whim (SW700500)

The largest of the buildings at the top of the cliff is the house of a dual-purpose 24-inch engine erected in 1872-3. The engine drove 32 heads of stamps and wound from Towanroath shaft on the cliffs below. The stack on the north (boiler house) side of the building is unusual in being entirely supported by the side wall. The engine (together with a single boiler) was put up for sale in 1887. Modified during the 1911-14 reworking, the house (Listed Grade II) was consolidated by the National Trust in 1986 without restoring the fallen wing wall lying across the top of the bob wall.

Immediately north of the engine house are the bases of the gas-engine driven stamps, and further NW (SW699501) that of the double-bayed calciner (Listed

Grade II) used to bake off impurities (mostly arsenic) in the tin ore. Both were installed during the 1911-14 reworking. An exposed portion of the calciner flue shows that it reused the stack of the all-enclosed whim. The distant chimney to the NE (SW703503) probably served a 60-inch pumping engine offered for sale in 1844.

whim installed in 1901 lies in undergrowth a short distance north. Little is known of the mine's early history, but records show production of 160 tons of copper ore in 1823-25, 280 tons in 1832-35 (as West Wheal Pink), and 440 tons of black tin in 1855-95. In the 20th century, Wheal Friendly was worked first as part of West Kitty Mine (until 1912) and finally as St. Agnes Consolidated. Overgrown remains of its dressing floors lurk in the valley below. The mine closed in 1916.

10. WEST WHEAL KITTY

West Kitty was the largest of several mines that worked beneath the town of St. Agnes. An amalgamation of many older workings that latterly included New Kitty (where the remaining engine house stands) and Wheal Friendly to the north, the mine operated under several names. West Kitty was first used for a reworking of an older sett (Wheal Rock) centred on Reynolds' shaft in 1863-71, following which the mine was immediately restarted as St. Agnes Consols, only to be renamed New St. Agnes in 1876. The mine's most profitable years followed its reopening as West Kitty in 1879, and from 1882 until its closure in 1913, the mine produced over 10,000 tons of black tin. It was taken over by St. Agnes Consolidated in 1912, but from mid-1913 all work was limited to Wheal Friendly. The mine later became part of unsuccessful attempts to reopen Wheal Kitty in 1929-30 and Polberro in 1937-41.

Thomas' Pumping Engine (SW720506)
In the heart of St. Agnes and now in a private garden off Vicarage Road, stands a well-preserved house (Listed Grade II)

Thomas' 40-inch pumping engine house at West Wheal Kitty in 2010 (above) and as it looked in 1967 (left) prior to the demolition of the house of Thomas' all-enclosed whim. The whim's separate stack (foreground right) survives.

The engine house of Reynolds' 28-inch whim at West Wheal Kitty prior to its demolition (1967).

of a 40-inch pumping engine erected on Thomas' shaft in 1895. Built by Harvey and Co. in 1863, the engine first worked at Wheal Hartley, near Gwinear, until the mine's closure in 1867. Prior to its erection at West Kitty, the engine had been standing idle at nearby West Polbreen since 1889, having been moved there from an unknown location (possibly by way of New Chiverton, near Perranwell) in 1885. In 1913, the engine was moved to Carpalla clay works in the St. Austell district, where it worked until 1944. In 1952, it was purchased by the Science Museum in London and is now in the museum's store at Wroughton, near Swindon. The house of the engine's two boilers stood alongside the west wall. Thomas' shaft reached a depth of 116 fathoms (212m).

Thomas' whim (SW719505)

In private grounds SW of the engine house at Thomas' shaft stands the graceful separate stack (Listed Grade II) of Thomas' whim, which was an all-enclosed engine erected in 1895 to wind from Thomas' shaft. Until its demolition in 1983 to make room for development, the engine house lay a short distance to the NE on the site now occupied by a large house. The house of the engine's single boiler lay alongside the south wall.

Reynolds' whim (SW719509)

Until it was demolished to make way for new housing, the engine house of Reynolds' 28-inch whim stood just south of the junction of Trevaunance Road and Brecon Close, its last vestiges disappearing only recently. The engine was erected in 1875 to wind from Reynolds' shaft some 100 metres to the south (close to the junction of Trevaunance Road and West Kitty). The house of the engine's single boiler stood against the west wall at right angles to the house. Reynolds' shaft, which was drained by a 50-inch pumping engine erected in 1872, reached a depth of about 120 fathoms (220m). It is said that this engine went to a St, Austell clay works but was never erected

11. POLBREEN MINE (SW718504)

Until their destruction to make way for housing developments, two engine houses marked the site of Polbreen Mine on the SW side of the St. Agnes. One of the oldest mines in the district, Polbreen was said to be haunted by the spirit of Dorcas, a local woman who committed suicide after her fiancée died in a mining accident. The mine was intermittently worked for tin and a little copper until 1874, when it was merged with West Kitty. Until the mid-1960s, the house of the mine's 36-inch pumping engine stood close to what is now the west end of Polbreen Avenue. Originally built by Perran Foundry, this was erected on North (or Vivian's) shaft (SW718504) in the 1880s when the mine was briefly reworked as New Polbreen or New Kitty. It had previously worked at Charlotte United Mine near Chapel Porth (where its house still stands) and, before that, at Wheal Freedom (across the valley from Charlotte United), where it was at work by 1854. Prior to the erection of Thomas' pumping engine at West Kitty, the engine also worked Thomas' shaft by

The 36-inch pumping engine house on North (or Vivian's) shaft at Polbreen Mine looking north (1964)

way of flat rods. It ended its days at Bloomdale clay works, near Foxhole, in the St. Austell district. North shaft reached a depth of 90 fathoms (165m). The house of the mine's stamps engine (presumably the 24-inch stamps and winding engine offered for sale at the time of the merger with West Kitty in 1875), was a familiar site near the western end of what is now Polbreen Lane (SW719503) until its demolition in 1971.

The stamps engine house (probably a 24-inch used for both stamping and winding) at Polbreen Mine looking ENE. The winding shaft is unknown but the house was aligned towards Dorcas's shaft to the east (1967).

The 50-inch pumping engine house at Gooninnis Mine in 2010, and (below) in 1967, the smaller stack is that of the horizontal whim.

12. GOONINNIS MINE (SW725505)

On private land overlooking St. Agnes from the SE, stand the prominent engine house and solitary castellated stack (both Listed Grade II) of Gooninnis Mine. This short-lived venture was started in 1898 in an attempt to locate the extension of West Kitty's main tin lode. But the trial was a failure and the mine closed in 1903 after going down 72 fathoms (132m) with no results. The engine house is that of a 50-inch pumping engine set to work on Engine (or Mary's) shaft in 1901. Built by Harvey and Co. for Penhalls Mine on the northern outskirts of St. Agnes in 1863, the engine was purchased by Trevaunance Mine (along with a single boiler) in 1884 and set to work the following year on Enys' shaft (where its stack still stands) before being moved to Gooninnis. In 1910, the engine was moved to Goonvean clay works in the St. Austell district where it worked until 1956. It is presently in

storage in Hayle where it is to become the centerpiece of a planned museum on the site of Harvey's Foundry. The engine house, with its picturesque mix of granite and slate, yellow (St. Day) brickwork, inward-flaring windows and castellated stack, closely resembles that at Wheal Friendly, which was built at about the same time. The boiler house stood alongside to the south. Damaged by a lightning strike, the attached stack was restored by the Duchy of Cornwall in 1992-93. Traces of the loading for a balance box at right angles to the engine house can be seen on the NE side of the filled shaft, which reached a final depth of 72 fathoms (132m). The solitary stack to the SW (SW724505) in that of the mine's 12-inch horizontal winding engine purchased from Holman Brothers in Camborne in 1899.

13. WHEAL KITTY (SW724513)

High above Trevaunance Combe north of St. Agnes, amid a complex of mine buildings on Goonlaze Downs that are now part of a small industrial estate, stands the tastefully restored engine house (Listed Grade II) of Sara's 65-inch pumping engine. Built as a 60-inch by Williams' Perran Foundry in 1852 for Deerpark Mine on the Great Perran Iron Lode, near Perranporth, the engine was later rebuilt as a 65-inch without a steam jacket. It was erected at Wheal Kitty in 1910 after standing idle for while at Tindene Mine, near Retallack, where it had been set to work in 1887. It stopped work when the mine closed in 1919, but was restarted in 1926 and worked until the mine's final closure in 1930. The engine was scrapped in 1938, but a piece of the bob is preserved

Two views of Sara's 65-inch pumping engine house at Wheal Kitty before (in 2000) and after (in 2010) its tasteful conversion to an office building.

Sara's 65-inch pumping engine house and roofed boiler house (right) at Wheal Kitty. The second stack is that of the Homan's horizontal winding engine (1967).

by the National Trust at East Pool. The restored boiler house for the engine's three boilers, which were set at right angles to the engine house, stands alongside to the north. The house of the mine's Holman's horizontal winding engine (with a conical roof) stands a short distance in front of the engine house.

Wheal Kitty was a rich tin mine formed by the merger of many smaller concerns that date to the mid-18th century and before. It was worked almost continuously from 1838 until 1919, producing copper and pyrite in addition to tin. It closed in 1904, but was merged with Penhalls Mine on the cliffs to the north and worked under the name Wheal Kitty and Penhalls United from 1907 to 1919. It was finally worked as Wheal Kitty Tin Ltd from 1926 until 1930, by which time Sara's shaft had been sunk to a depth of 158 fathoms (290m).

14. BLUE HILLS MINE (SW728517)

In Trevellas Combe, east of Goonlaze Downs, stands the picturesque 60-inch pumping engine house and separate stack (both Listed Grade II) of Blue Hills Mine. Formed in 1810 from the merger of several older tin workings, the mine was originally worked until 1819. It was reopened in about 1858 and over the next 40 years produced over 2100 tons of black tin. In 1879, it came under the management of neighbouring Penhalls Mine, with which it was connected underground. It became a separate entity again in 1893 and closed in 1897. The mine was briefly reworked with Wheal Kitty early in the 20th century. Little is know of the pumping engine beyond its size, but it was erected in 1869 and worked until the mine's closure. The house has few windows and is constructed entirely of slate with no granite cornerstones, suggesting a shortage of cash at the time it was built. The loadings for a balance box at right angles to the engine house can be seen on the north side of the filled shaft. The house of the engine's two boilers lay alongside to the north. Engine shaft reached a depth of about 80 fathoms (146m).

The massive masonry ruins to the north of the engine house (SW728516) are the crankshaft and flywheel loadings of the mine's single-cylinder horizontal whim /stamps engine. The loadings contain slots for a pair of flywheels with a winding drum pit to the south. The boiler house was on the east side with the separate stack on the hillside (SW728518) serving both engines. At Blue Hills Tin, a short distance up Trevellas Combe, a restored waterwheel-driven set of Cornish stamps serves a small tin streaming and smelting operation run as a visitor attraction by the Wills family.

The 60-inch pumping engine house and separate stack at Blue Hills Mine (2010).

The 60-inch pumping engine house at Blue Hills Mine. The masonry in front of the bob wall is the loading for the balance box (1967). (right) Ten heads of waterwheel-driven Cornish stamps now restored to operating conditions at Blue Hills Tin (1967).

Tolvaddon Valley viewed north from Tuckingmill in 1964, prior to the construction of the Redruth-Camborne bypass. The large engine house (left) housed the 70-inch pumping engine at Wheal Seton (now demolished), whereas that in the middle distance (right) is East Pool's Tolvaddon ("Henrietta") stamps. The larger stacks are those of arsenic flues.

CHAPTER 7 Camborne – Redruth Mining District

The immensely prosperous Camborne-Redruth mining district occupies the north side of Carn Brea between these two hugely important 19th century mining centres. The district straddles the northern boundary of the Carn Brea granite, which, at surface, more-or-less follows the railway line ENE between the two towns. Many of the mineral lodes, which run parallel to the edge of the granite, were fabulously rich in copper in the country rock near the surface, and equally rich in tin in the granite at depth, and were exploited by some of the richest and deepest mines in the county. Between them, for example, the mines of Dolcoath, East Pool and Agar, and Carn Brea and Tincroft produced over 800,000 tons of copper ore and almost 180,000 tons of black tin. The district was also home to some of the principal figures in the development of Cornish mining technology (including Richard Trevithick) and had its own School of Mines in Camborne, which was instrumental in the export of this technology abroad. Copper mining, which dominated the district's initial production, was replaced by deeper tin mining following the mid-19th century collapse in copper prices, allowing many of the mines to survive into the twentieth century. East Pool and Agar survived until 1945 and South Crofty, the last of the Cornish tin mines, closed in 1998. Although many of the original mine sites and most of their engine houses have been cleared by 20th century development, the Mineral Tramways Project embodies recent efforts to conserve what remains of the region's mining landscape, and the district still preserves three beam engines on their original sites in the care of the National Trust – Michell's 30-inch whim and Taylor's 90-inch pumping engine at East Pool and Agar Mine, and Robinson's 80-inch pumping engine at South Crofty.

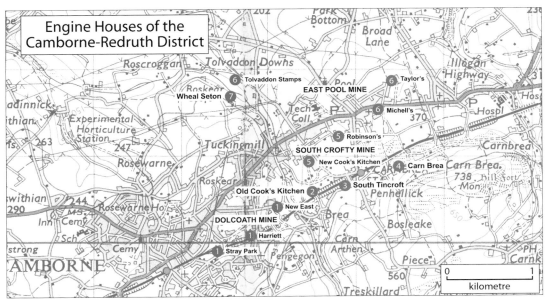

The surviving 65-inch pumping engine house of Dolcoath Mine at Stray Park, viewed from the boiler house side (2010).

1. DOLCOATH MINE

Known affectionately as the "Queen of Cornish Mines", Dolcoath was an incredibly rich and long-lived mine with an output exceeding 350,000 tons of copper ore and 100,000 tons of black tin. Worked for copper from the early 1700s until a price slump forced its closure in1788, the mine was reopened in 1799 to become the most important copper producer in Cornwall. When its copper reserves became exhausted in the mid-1840s, the discovery of rich tin deposits at depth gave the mine a second lease of life as the county's most important tin producer. Although little can be seen of its former greatness today, Dolcoath went on to become the largest and deepest mine in Cornwall, with two of its principal shafts – New Sump (on which the first true Cornish beam engine was erected in 1816) and Williams (completed in 1912) – reaching the 550-fathom (1,006m) level. The mine finally closed in 1921. An attempt to reopen its northern section as New Dolcoath Mine (1923-29) met with little success and, in 1936, the sett was purchased by neighbouring South Crofty.

Stray Park Pumping Engine (SW654399)

East of Camborne town centre beside the railway line on Park Lane is the conserved house (with shortened stack) of the 65-inch pumping engine at Stray Park Mine, which Dolcoath acquired in 1870. Originally a 60-inch purchased from Pentireglaze Mine, near Padstow, in 1857, the engine was later re-cylindered to 64 - inches. In 1900, it was almost entirely rebuilt (along with its house) by Holman Bros. with a 65-inch cylinder. Only the engine's main beam was retained. The original engine (together with a 24-inch whim bought from East Wheal Rose in 1858) was installed over the main (Machine or Engine) shaft with the intent of deepening the mine in search for tin. Prior to this, the mine had been a significant copper producer with output records dating to 1827. However, production failed to meet the outlay costs and, following a series of accidents that caused the mine to flood in 1868-69, the mine was put up for sale as a going concern in August 1870. Under Dolcoath ownership, the engine was worked until the mine closed in 1921, and was finally broken up around 1938. Inside the engine house is the cylinder bedstone with holes for six holding-down bolts. The house for the engine's four boilers, the roofline of which can still be seen, stood on the east side with the boilers arranged perpendicular to the engine house. Machine shaft ultimately reached a depth of 413 fathoms (755m).

Harriett Pumping Engine (SW658401)

On the east side of Camborne near the Lower Pengegon railway crossing is the conserved engine house (with stack missing its upper brickwork) of the 65-inch pumping engine at Harriett shaft (Listed Grade II). Built as a 60-inch engine by Perran Foundry in 1860, the engine was re-cylindered to 65-inches in 1885. The engine worked until the mine closed in 1921 and was finally scrapped around 1938. The house for the engine's three boilers, a part of the front wall of which still stands, stood on the west side, opposite the balance box, the loadings for which were visible when the shaft was open. Harriett shaft ultimately reached the 490-fathom (896m) level. The winding drum in front of the house is that of the shaft's horizontal steam hoist built by Worsley Mesnes of Wigan and set to work in 1897. This operated skips for the miners and replaced the mine's man engine installed in 1854, which worked in

The surviving 65-inch pumping engine houses at Harriett shaft, viewed from the boiler house side (2010).

a shaft a short distance to the WNW. In 1924 the original single drum winder was transferred to New Dolcoath Mine in Roskear where it was equipped with a second drum and worked until the mine closed in 1929. The drum was re-erected on its original foundations in 2009.

New East Winding Engine (SW661404)

Standing beside Dolcoath Road south of Tuckingmill is the modified house (Listed Grade II) of a rotative beam engine used to raise ore from New East shaft a short distance to the WSW and also to pump water from adit level for the mine's

The engine house of New East whim at Dolcoath Mine modified for use as an electrical substation showing filled opening in bob wall (2010).

stamps and dressing floors using an auxiliary "back bob". The pumping shaft was immediately behind the house. In 1894, the whim was replaced by a horizontal steam winder (purchased secondhand from the Wheal Cock section of Botallack Mine) and the engine house became derelict. In 1913, however, it was converted to an electrical substation, at which time the bob opening was filled and given a new doorway, the boiler house door was bricked in, the cylinder opening was modified, and terracotta piping for electrical cables was inserted into the building's gable ends. The original boiler house was demolished. New East shaft reached the 440-fathom (805m) level.

2. OLD COOK'S KITCHEN MINE

Old Cook's Kitchen Mine began as a small but profitable copper mine in the early 1700s and went on to become one of the area's richest, deepest and most long-lived. It is believed to have got its name from a miner called Cook who described the lode he discovered there as being as wide as his kitchen. It was rich enough to weather the slump in copper prices caused by the massive discovery at Parys Mountain on Anglesey in the 1780s and, in the years that followed, was one of the most productive mines in Cornwall. But by the 1830s, production levels and the grade of the ore were falling and, despite the discovery and production of tin from about 1835, the mine closed in 1848. However, it was reopened in 1849 with the intent of finding large deposits of tin at depth, and from 1854 tin production progressively replaced that of copper. Over the next 40 years, almost 9,000 tons of black tin were raised, but the mine struggled to be profitable and, in 1895, it was amalgamated with neighbouring Tincroft, which was itself amalgamated with Carn Brea Mine in 1896. The mine closed in 1913, by which time it had reached a depth of 430 fathoms (768m), second only to Dolcoath.

Chapple's pumping engine and whim (SW665406)

Beside the railway line north of Brea stand the heavily iron-trussed engine houses of Chapple's 55-inch pumping engine (with a separate stack lacking its upper brickwork) and 26-inch whim (both Listed Grade II). The pumping engine was originally a 50-inch that was re-cylindered to 55-inches around 1872. It was at work in 1838 and it is likely that the house dates from this period. The footings of the boiler house (for two boilers) lie alongside to the east and the loadings for the balance box can be seen

Two views of Chapple's 55-inch pumping engine house (with separate stack) and 26-inch whim at Old Cook's Kitchen Mine (2010 and 1967).

on the east side of shaft. The winding engine, which drew from the same shaft, dates from about 1860 and until 1888, pulled an iron bucket or kibble rather than a skip, which limited hoisting capacity. The house lacks its north wall, which adjoined the house of the engine's single boiler. Despite their proximity to the Mineral Tramway, neither engine house has been consolidated and both are in danger of collapse – the iron strengthening indicating a concern for their deteriorating condition while they were still at work. Although the whim can be accessed, permission to visit the pumping engine house must be sought from South Crofty on whose fenced property the house now lies. The base of the Harvey-built horizontal man engine lies largely buried just to the south of the whim. Chapple's shaft reached a depth of 430 fathoms (786m) below adit.

The engine house of the 26-inch man engine whim at South Tincroft (2010).

3. TINCROFT MINE

Like Cook's Kitchen Mine, Tincroft started as a small but rich 18th century copper mine (the earliest records dating to the 1680s) that later changed to tin. Tincroft's copper, however, held out longer and the gradual switch to tin production did not take place until the 1860s. But by the 1870s it had become a rich tin mine. It was worked in two sections, North and South, but the site of North Tincroft has been entirely obliterated by modern development. In 1895 the mine acquired neighbouring Cook's Kitchen, but was amalgamated with Carn Brea Mine in 1896. Tincroft ceased underground operations in 1921, by which time it had reached the 350-fathom (640m) level.

South Tincroft man engine whim (SW669407)

Beside Tincroft Road NE of Brea is the engine house (Listed Grade II) of the 26-inch winding engine thought to have been installed sometime after 1860 to draw from Downright shaft beyond the railway to the NNW and/or from Dunkin's shaft in front of the engine house loadings. The latter became Man Engine shaft when the engine was also set to drive a man engine by way of a second crank, gearing and flat rods. This was operating to the 142-fathom (260m) level in 1874, and to at least the 170-fathom (311m) level by 1880. By about 1891, it had ceased operation although the beam engine continued to function as a whim. This is now the only complete man engine house left in Cornwall. The loadings in front of the house show the former position of the flywheel and winding drum, as well as the reduction gearing between the crankshaft and the shaft which carried the crank that

The engine house of the 26-inch man engine whim at South Tincroft, showing the house and separate stack of the horizontal steam-driven air compressor engine (1967).

drove the flat-rods. The barred hole at the base of the bob wall is for the eccentric rods, which worked the valve gear off the main crankshaft. Inside, the cylinder bedstones are in place as are some of the holding-down bolts and one corner of the cylinder bottom. A pair of depressions on the west side of the building mark the site of the engine's two boilers, the second one added in 1897. Dunkin's (Man Engine) shaft eventually reached the 320-fathom (585m) level. The nearby building to the ENE (also Listed Grade II) housed a horizontal steam-driven cross-compound air compressor built by Harvey's of Hayle in 1891, which powered the underground rock drills. The stack and base of the house of the compressor's single boiler lies alongside to the north.

4. CARN BREA MINE

Carn Brea Mine came into existence with the amalgamation of several smaller concerns in 1832. Like its neighbours, the mine started as a copper producer and in the 1840s it was the richest copper mine in the county. It continued to be a significant copper producer into the 1870s, but by the late 1850s, greater profits were being obtained from tin. In 1896, the mine amalgamated with neighbouring Tincroft and Cook's Kitchen to form Carn Brea and Tincroft mines. This was a vast operation with significant output of tin, copper and arsenic. But it was a financial failure and in 1913 the Carn Brea section closed. Over its lifetime, the mine produced 470,000 tons of copper ore

Two views of the 32-inch (old) stamps engine house at Carn Brea Mine. The lower view also shows the separate stack of the nearby 34-inch (new) stamps engine (2010 and 1967).

and 53,000 tons of black tin, and its deepest shaft (Highburrow East) had reached the 390-fathoms (713m) level.

Carn Brea stamps (SW675409)

At the foot of Carn Brea just east of Tregajorran, the consolidated engine house of Carn Brea stamps with its separate stepped chimney is among the oldest in Cornwall. It housed a 32-inch stamps engine (Old Stamps) that was erected in 1837 and worked until the mine closed in 1913. The engine also re-circulated water for the dressing floors and was single acting with a weight box strapped to the nose of the bob to perform the outdoor stroke. Formerly, a tramway linked the stamps to Highburrow East shaft (the original site of the 90-inch pumping engine now preserved at East Pool and Agar) across the railway to the NW. There is now no sign of the engine's

Michell's 30-inch winding engine at East Pool Mine (2010).

Members of the Cornish Engine's Preservation Society (now the Trevithick Society) gathered at Michell's 30-inch winding engine at East Pool Mine in 1964, before the boiler house was rebuilt.

speed of 1,000 feet per minute (5.1 metres per second). The engine worked until a major underground collapse in 1921 rendered Michell's shaft, which was sunk on the incline to the 252-fathom (461 metres) level, unusable. It was saved from being scrapped in 1941 and has been in the care of the National Trust since 1967. In 1975 it was set into motion again and is now open to the public and run on electricity throughout the summer months. The original boiler house was demolished after the mine closed, but was rebuilt by the National Trust in 1975 and contains a Cornish boiler similar to the one the engine originally possessed. Formerly at the Poor Law Institution of the Truro Union (where it provided steam for the laundry), the present boiler was made by Messrs Ruston and Hornsby in Lincoln. The brick portion of the stack was recently replaced after being struck by lightning.

Two views of the Tolvaddon (Henrietta) 24-inch stamps engine house at East Pool Mine (2010 and 1964).

installed in Cornwall. Built by Holman Brothers in 1887 to the design of Francis W. Michell, it was known as East Pool North whim and wound from Michell's shaft about 40 metres to the NE at a

Tolvaddon stamps (SW656419)

On the east side of Tolvaddon Valley (see page 100) north of the A30, and well to the NW of the engine houses at Pool, is the modified house of Tolvaddon (Henrietta) 24-inch stamps engine. This was the smaller of two batteries of stamps belonging to East Pool's extensive ore processing plant in the Tolvaddon Valley, which operated from the 1860s until the mine closed in 1945. From 1903, ore was transported here from the mine by the electric, passenger-carrying, Camborne and Redruth Tramway, an earlier electric overhead conveyor system having proved to be a failure. After the line closed in 1934, the ore was carried more directly on an aerial ropeway that was in use until 1945. The engine drove 32 heads of stamps and is believed to have originally belonged to Wheal Emily Henrietta (which closed in 1873), on whose sett it stands. It was taken over by East Pool in 1883, presumably having stood idle for a decade. Subsequently modified for other uses, the bob opening has been blocked up with concrete and an additional doorway added to the SE wall.

7. WHEAL SETON (SW656419)

Until its destruction in 1975 as part of the Scorrier-Camborne road expansion, the imposing 70-inch pumping engine house at Wheal Seton (noteworthy for its flat roof) was a familiar landmark on

The 70-inch pumping engine house at Wheal Seton prior to its demolition in 1975 (1964).

the west side of Tolvaddon Valley north of Tuckingmill (see page 100). Erected on Tregoning's shaft, the engine was built by the Copperhouse Foundry of Hayle in 1851. In 1874, it was removed to the Tinsley Coal Company's colliery near Rotherham together with its two boilers (housed alongside the west side wall). Principally a copper mine with production records going back to 1834, Wheal Seton stopped working in 1873 and closed in 1876. The main shaft (Tilly's) reached the 210-fathom (384m) level.

Consolidated engine houses of Fortescue's 90-inch pumping engine (left) and 28-inch whim (right) at Wheal Grenville.

CHAPTER 8 Troon – Carnkie Mining District

The immensely prosperous Troon-Carnkie mining district runs ENE along the south side of Carn Brea, following the course of the Great Flat Lode in a narrow corridor between the Carn Brea and Carnmenellis granites. The lode was so-named because it is tilted at a gentle angle of about 30 degrees to the horizontal unlike most Cornish lodes, which are steep. This rich ore body, which yielded almost exclusively tin, was discovered around 1870 and provided a huge boost to the region's economy since it came at a time when the shallower, but immensely rich copper deposits had become exhausted and the mining industry was in decline. In the event, only the more solvent mines were able to take advantage of the discovery because the narrow, twisting shafts of the shallower copper mines were unsuitable for the development of the new lode. The 3-6 metre wide Great Flat Lode ultimately produced over 90,000 tons of black tin and was worked by some of the most important mines in Cornwall. The exploitation of tin allowed these mines to continue production well into the twentieth century in a region that has since remained relatively undisturbed. As a result, the mining district preserves the greatest concentration of engine houses anywhere in Cornwall.

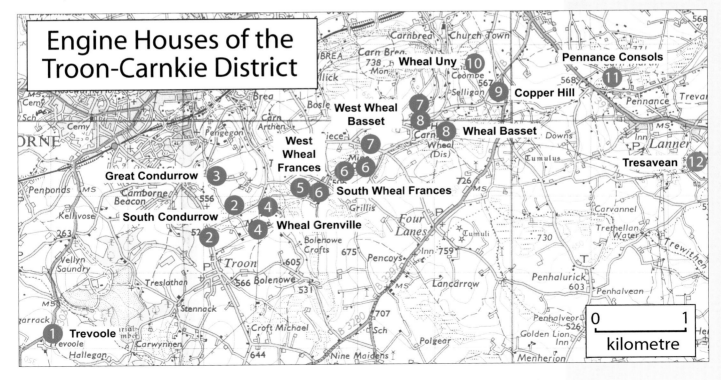

Engine Houses of the Troon-Carnkie District

Two views of the 70-inch pumping engine house at Trevoole Mine. The separate stack is that of the mine's 23-inch horizontal whim (2010).

of the Great Flat Lode proved false. The lone stack nearby (also Listed Grade II) is that of the mine's 23-inch horizontal winding engine, which was erected at the same time and may have come from South Caradon Mine, near Liskeard, along with two boilers. Prior to this, records of copper production date from the late 1820s to the 1840s, with a significant period of reworking in 1856-61, during which over 3700 tons of copper ore were raised. The filled balance box pit of the pumping engine is now part of a garden alongside the former boiler house, the roofline of which can be traced on the SW wall of the engine house. Engine shaft reached the 130-fathom (238m) level.

1. TREVOOLE MINE (SW638371)

Sitting in the grounds of a recent development beside the B3303 between Camborne and Praze is the imposing house (Listed Grade II) of a 70-inch pumping engine erected on this copper mine during a short-lived reopening for tin in 1886-91 under the name of West Wheal Grenville. However, reports that the mine was underlain by an extension

2. SOUTH CONDURROW (KING EDWARD) MINE

The history of South Condurrow begins in 1850 when its predecessor, Old Tye Mine, was renamed. Prior to this, the mine was worked briefly before closing in 1830 and had been reopened with Great Condurrow in 1844. As South Condurrow, it was first worked for copper, but its most productive years start with the discovery of the western end of the Great Flat Lode in 1870. Although plagued by flooding, the mine became the most profitable in the entire Carn Brea region in 1878 and it continued to pay dividends until 1893. Marshall's shaft was sunk in 1881, but this was not a successful development and the mine closed in 1896 as a result of the falling price of tin. An attempt to open up the mine's western end, around Marshall's shaft, in 1899-03 proved unsuccessful and ownership passed to Wheal Grenville. Prior to this, in 1897, the older (eastern) section of the mine had been presented to the Camborne School of Mines for training purposes. Renamed King Edward Mine on the accession of Edward VII in 1901, the facility was equipped with workshops, lecture rooms, a survey office and a small mill containing the latest ore-dressing equipment. The closure of Wheal Grenville in 1920 caused King Edward Mine to flood and underground operations were transferred to adjacent Great Condurrow Mine, above water level to the north. The mill and its equipment, much of which has been restored to working order, is now the centrepiece of a museum that opened in 2002 as part of the Mineral Tramways Project.

Engine house of Marshall's 60-inch pumping engine at South Condurrow Mine (2010).

Marshall's Pumping Engine and Whim (SW660385)

Standing beside the main road on the northern outskirts of Troon are the consolidated engine houses (both Listed Grade II) of a 26-inch whim and 60-inch pumping engine erected on Marshall's shaft in 1881 (the year the shaft was started) and 1886, respectively. Both engines were secondhand, the whim having been acquired from West Chiverton Mine near Zelah, whereas the pumping engine, which was set to work in 1888, had previously served on Giles Engine shaft at Wheal Jane, near Truro (where it had been erected secondhand in 1881). Acquired by Wheal Grenville in

Two views of the engine houses of Marshall's 26-inch winding engine (foreground) and 60-inch pumping engine at South Condurrow Mine (2010 and 1968).

the capped shaft. The outer wall of the house of the whim's single boiler stands alongside to the SE and the loadings for the flywheel and winding drum, which worked a double skip road, are prominent at the foot of the bob wall. Marshall's shaft is 175 fathoms (320m) deep.

King Edward Whim (SW664389)

To the NE, in the grounds of the King Edward Mine Museum, is the conserved engine house (Listed Grade II) and modified boiler house (for two boilers) of a 25-inch winding engine moved from some other location on the mine and re-erected here to hoist from Engine shaft (a short distance to the north) in 1868. When South Condurrow closed, the engine was used by King Edward Mine until it was replaced in 1908 by a horizontal steam hoist built by Holman Bros. This engine later went to Castle-an-Dinas Mine, near St. Austell, where it worked until 1957, but it was re-erected on its original site in 2003 as part of the King Edward Mine Museum. Plans exist to use the beam engine house to re-erect the Rostowrack engine, presently on site but dismantled. This 22-inch rotative engine built by West and Son of St. Blazey in 1851 was installed at Rostowrack clay works, near St. Austell, in 1861, where it worked pumps for 91 years.

South Condurrow Stamps (SW663389)

Northwest of the museum complex stands the secured house (Listed Grade II) of an engine of unknown size erected to drive 48 heads of stamps in 1869. This number was later increased to 64 in 1871 and possibly as many as 96 in 1872. Latterly used by Great Condurrow Mine, the

1903, the pumping engine was kept at work until that mine closed in 1920. It was finally scrapped in 1923. Both engine houses contain their cylinder bedstones, and the masonry walls for the pumping engine's balance box have been consolidated on the boiler house side of

engine was worked until 1909. Slots secured by gratings for the crank and twin flywheels are prominent in front of the bob wall, which has been reinforced with tie rods. The boiler house (with two boilers) stood across the rear of the engine house.

3. GREAT CONDURROW MINE (SW661393)

Also known simply as Condurrow, Great Condurrow Mine dates from 1815 and was worked for copper until 1830. Reopened in 1844, it was worked for both copper and tin until 1873. Attempts to rework the mine as Pendarves United in 1880-81 and Condurrow United in 1906-14 were unsuccessful. The surviving engine house dates from this last reworking.

The all-granite engine house (Listed Grade II) stands beside Condurrow Road in Higher Condurrow and was erected on Woolf's (renamed Neame's) shaft in 1906 for an 80-inch pumping engine set to work

Engine houses of the 25-inch winding engine at King Edward Mine (top) and the stamps at South Condurrow (2010).

House of Woolf's (Neame's) 80-inch pumping engine at Great Condurrow Mine showing a portion of the boiler house wall (left) and supports at the base of the bob wall for the condenser cistern (1968).

in 1907. Built by Harvey and Co. (engineers Loam and Son, Liskeard) in 1868 for West Chiverton Mine, near Perranzabuloe, and set to work on Batters' shaft (where its house still stands) the following year, the engine was described as one of the most finished and perfect engines ever made in Cornwall. It was re-purchased by Harvey and Co. in 1882 and stored at Hayle foundry until 1899 when it was re-erected for pumping dressing water on Garland's shaft at Gwennap United Mines (where its bob wall still stands). Here it worked for only seven months before being offered for sale in 1905. The house at Condurrow was first started on the opposite (north) side of the shaft but was removed to its present site because the ground was found to be weak. The engine's four new Holman boilers were housed on the east side. Granite supports at the base of the bob wall are for the condenser cistern, and the filled balance box pit can be seen west of the open shaft, which is protected by a grating. The engine was scrapped in 1916. Woolf's shaft is 283 fathoms (518m) deep.

4. WHEAL GRENVILLE (GRENVILLE UNITED)

Located at the western end of the Great Flat Lode, Wheal Grenville first came into existence in 1845 when it was granted a lease to take over the workings of a number of older copper mines (including Newton Moor and Polgine) that had been intermittently active since the 1790s. The

House of Woolf's (Neame's) 80-inch pumping engine at Great Condurrow Mine (2010).

venture initially proved unsuccessful and the mine was sold in 1855. But as the mine deepened in the 1860s, shallower copper was progressively replaced by more profitable tin. Yet the mine continued to struggle in the face of falling tin values until, under new management, North (later Goold's) shaft intersected the Great Flat Lode in 1877. From this point on, the mine's fortunes changed and profits steadily soared, peaking in 1893-94. In 1903, Wheal Grenville acquired South Condurrow Mine, and in 1906, it was amalgamated with part of West Wheal Frances to form Grenville United Mines. Hurt by a loss of skilled labour during World War I and the fall in tin prices that followed it, Grenville United closed in 1920.

Fortescue's Pumping Engine and Whim (SW668389)

East of the King Edward Mine Museum stand the consolidated engine houses of the 90-inch pumping engine and 28-inch whim (both Listed Grade II) erected on Fortescue's shaft in 1892. The whim is of uncertain parentage, but is thought to have previously worked at South Roskear Mine in Camborne. The pumping engine was originally built by Harvey and Co. in 1872 for a colliery in South Wales but was never erected. Instead, it remained stored at Harvey's foundry in Hayle until 1881 when it was fitted with a longer bob (the original having been used in the 90-inch engine supplied to East Wheal Rose in 1881) to enable it to be erected in an

Two views of the engine houses of Fortescue's 90-inch pumping engine (foreground) and 28-inch whim at Wheal Grenville. The engine house in the background (below) is that of Grenville New Stamps (2010 and below in 1968).

existing engine house at Tresavean Mine, near Lanner. In 1892, it was moved to Fortescue's Shaft where it worked until the mine closed in 1920. In 1922, the engine was moved to New Cook's Kitchen Shaft at South Crofty where it worked until it was wrecked in 1950 when one side of the extended bob broke in two. The

short stack was originally taller, but was damaged in a lightning strike in 1897. The soleplate and stools for the main beam on top of the bob wall where re-erected here when the engine house at New Cook's Kitchen shaft was demolished to make room to pre-erect new headgear in 1983. Wall plates with the name "Tavistock Iron Works" occur on both engine houses. Fortescue's shaft is 395 fathoms (722m) deep, measured not vertically but on the underlie (see also page 116).

New Stamps (SW665386)

Standing prominently on the southern slopes of the valley NE of Troon is the engine house (Listed Grade II) of Grenville New stamps, which held a 36-inch engine bought third-hand from West Condurrow Mine. It had originally been

supplied to an unsuccessful gold mine in North Wales in 1864 and later worked at Nangiles Mine near Twelveheads. The house and associated dressing floors below it were constructed in 1891 to provide Wheal Grenville with new ore treatment facilities, with the engine driving 136 heads of stamps in 1892. The massive crankshaft loading at the base of the bob wall contains pits for the condenser, crank, and two flywheels, the slots for which extend into the bob wall (see page 18). The masonry plinth in front carried an auxiliary bob, which was worked off the main beam and used to pump water for the dressing floors from a small shaft in front of the loadings. Inside the house (see page 14), one of the cylinder bedstones and four holding-down bolts survive in place. The boiler house, part of the roofline of which can be seen on the back wall, stood at the rear with its three boilers arranged transversely. The long flat building immediately below is the Frue vanner house, which was built in 1900 to house Holman's vanning (shaking) tables used to separate the ore. The small stack to the west is that of the arsenic flue.

Goold's Pumping Engine (SW664387)

Wantonly demolished in the early 1970s, little now remains of Goold's engine house, which stood across the road from the King Edward Mine Museum. This was erected on North (renamed Goold's) shaft in 1877 for a new 80-inch pumping engine built by Harvey and Co. to the design of Hocking and Loam and set to work in 1878. In 1906 the 23-ton bob broke in the centre and a heavier 38-ton replacement was ordered from Holman Bros. The engine was finally scrapped in 1928. The engine's boiler house (with four boilers) lay on the west side. Goold's shaft was sunk almost to the 320-fathom (585m) level, 250 fathoms (457m) below surface.

Two views of New Stamps engine house at Grenville United (2010 and 1968).

Goold's 80-inch pumping engine at Grenville United before its demolition with the engine houses of South Condurrow stamps (left) and King Edward whim in the background (1968).

Two views of Bailey's 24-inch winding engine house at West Wheal Frances with (right) Daubuz' engine house at South Wheal Frances in the background (2010 and 1961 by Kenneth Brown).

5. WEST WHEAL FRANCES (SW672391)

Standing alone on Newton Moor is the diminutive (two-floored) engine house (Listed Grade II) of Bailey's 24-inch winding engine erected in 1869 to hoist from Smith's shaft (a short distance to the WSW), which had been started the same year. It later operated stamps. The mine was started in 1848, but only from the mid-1860s was tin production significant and sales usually failed to meet production costs, so it was rarely profitable. It was abandoned in 1896 following a major slump in tin prices, and the whim was put up for sale in 1898. At some point the lower half of all the bottom floor openings were filled and the driving floor concreted over, so that the house could be used as a water tank. The house of the engine's single boiler stood alongside to the south. Smith's shaft reached the 174-fathom (318m) level at a depth of about 117 fathoms (214m) below surface.

6. SOUTH WHEAL FRANCES

Like other mines in the district, South Wheal Frances began as a successful copper mine. Although active in the early 1820s, it was first seriously worked with its reopening in 1834 and subsequent development in the early 1840s. Copper production rose to a peak in 1858, but then declined and had virtually ceased by 1873. In 1876 the Great Flat Lode was intersected in a level driven from Pascoe's shaft. However, the transition to significant tin production did not take place until the late 1870s and was never profitable. Although Marriot's shaft intersected the Great Flat Lode in 1886, the mine remained beset by financial troubles and, prompted by boundary disputes and serious flooding problems, it amalgamated with neighbouring West Basset in 1892 to form South Frances United, and all crushing and ore dressing was transferred to West Basset stamps. But this concern fared little better and, with losses exacerbated by a fire that seriously damaged the 80-inch pumping engine on Marriot's shaft, the mine was merged with Wheal Basset in 1896 to form Basset Mines Ltd. This consortium initially did well and Marriot's shaft was massively re-equipped and refurbished to a depth of 340 fathoms (622m). But it never reached its target depth of 5,000 feet (1,524m) and, with declining ore grade and a slump in tin prices, Basset Mines closed in 1918. From 1844 until 1891, South Frances produced almost 67,900 tons of copper ore and over 6,900 tons of black tin.

Daubuz' Multipurpose Engine (SW674390)

On the southwestern outskirts of Treskillard is the engine house (Listed Grade II) of a 30-inch rotative engine erected in 1880 to both wind and pump (by way of a short run of flat rods) from Daubuz' shaft about 60 metres to the WSW. The engine continued to be used after the mine's merger with Wheal Basset and ceased work only when Basset Mines closed in 1918. The house contains the cylinder bedstones and has extensive loadings in front of the bob wall that supported the crankshaft, flywheel, winding drum and flat rod gearing. The boiler house, the ruined walls of which still stand, held two boilers and lay on the south side opposite the wide, attached stack.

Two views of Daubuz' 30-inch multipurpose engine house at South Wheal Frances (2010).

Two views of the engine houses of Pascoe's 80-inch pumping engine (right) and 30-inch whim at South Wheal Frances. The bob wall in the background (below) is that of Thomas's engine at West Wheal Basset (2010 and 1968).

Pascoe's Pumping Engine and Whim (SW676395)

The pair of engine houses NE of Treskillard (both Listed Grade II) are those of the 30-inch whim and 80-inch pumping engine erected on Pascoe's shaft in 1879 and 1887, respectively. The house of the winding engine is particularly well preserved with its cylinder bedstones, extensive loadings at the foot of the bob wall for the flywheel and winding drum, and an almost complete boiler house alongside to the SE that held the engine's two boilers. The pumping engine was the largest ever built by St. Austell Foundry and first served Old Shepherd's Mine, near Newlyn East, in 1881. In 1916, with the engine drawing from the 340-fathom (622m) level, the top of the piston rod broke and the engine was wrecked. The engine parts were replaced by Worsley Mesnes of Wigan (who also built the horizontal whim for Harriett's shaft at Dolcoath) and, using the original bob, the engine continued to work until the mine closed in 1918. The house contains the engine's cylinder bedstones. Its unusual slit windows were probably adopted in the belief that smaller windows added strength to the walls.

Marriott's Shaft Complex (SW680395)

The complex of buildings (Listed Grade II) surrounding Marriott's shaft east of Pascoe's pumping engine and whim is one of the best-preserved examples of Cornish mining activity at the turn of the 20th century. It dates from the shaft's refurbishment under the ownership of Basset Mines in 1897-1900 and, although it includes no Cornish engine houses (the 80-inch pumping engine that formerly worked here having been destroyed by fire in 1895), it does include the house of an inverted compound beam engine (the only one of its kind in Cornwall) and that of a large horizontal whim. The house of the beam engine (the tallest in the complex) held a then state-of-the-art pumping engine built by Hathorn Davey and Co. of Leeds to the design of Henry Davey that was set to work in 1899. The bob was below floor level and was raised and lowered by two inverted cylinders situated at either end on the floor above. Instead of being cast, the bob was composed of riveted steel plates. A 40-inch high-pressure cylinder was connected to the bob near its nose (which extended out over the shaft through an arched opening), and passed its exhaust steam to an 80-inch low-pressure cylinder (taken from the earlier pumping engine) that was attached to the other end of the bob. The engine occupied the left hand side of the house (as viewed from the shaft), the large size of the house reflecting a provision to add a second engine of similar type alongside. In 1909, the original 32-ton bob, the rivets of which kept working loose, failed and was replaced by one of 55 tons made by Alexander Findlay and Co. of Motherwell,

Engine houses of the horizontal whim (right) and inverted compound beam engine (left) in the Marriot's shaft complex at South Wheal Frances (2010).

Lanarkshire. The engine worked until the mine closed in 1918 and was scrapped shortly thereafter. The winding engine house east of the covered shaft contained a compound horizontal engine built by Holman Bros. in 1900, with 23-inch high-pressure and 43-inch low-pressure cylinders, and a conical winding drum designed for faster hoisting. The boiler house that stands between the two buildings held six Lancashire boilers, which generated steam for the entire complex. Other buildings west of the pumping engine house include those of a Reidler air compressor for the underground rock drills (driven by a cross-compound horizontal engine built by Frazer and Chalmers of Erith, Kent), and the core of an ore crusher and sorter. The building immediately south was built in 1906 for a small steam capstan used to lift heavy equipment in the shaft and drive the ore crusher. South of the winding engine is the miners' dry (or changing house) built in 1908.

Thomas's 60-inch pumping engine house at West Wheal Basset (2010).

7. WEST WHEAL BASSET

Although worked previously under the names Wheal Charmer and Wheal Haste, West Wheal Basset came into being in 1846, but only became a major producer with the formation of a new company in the early 1850s. Like its neighbour South Frances, it was a rich copper mine, but was never able to make a profitable transition to tin following its discovery of the Great Flat Lode in 1869, largely because of poor management and inadequate stamping capacity. Copper production rose rapidly to a peak in 1857, but then gradually declined to almost nothing by the late 1870s, whereas tin production peaked in 1879 and then fell steadily until 1892, when the two mines were amalgamated. Between 1852 and 1891 the mine produced almost 86,000 tons of copper and over 10,000 tons of black tin.

Thomas's Pumping Engine (SW 681397)

Standing prominently beside the road from Piece to Four Lanes is the ruin of the 60-inch pumping engine house erected on Thomas's shaft in 1854, as indicated by a date stone on the dressed granite bob wall. The boiler house lay alongside to the NE. This was the mine's eastern pumping unit and is the oldest surviving engine house on the Great Flat Lode. The iron reinforcement dates from its final years.

The engine suffered a fire in 1896 that bent the piston rod, after which it was worked slowly to provide water for the West Basset dressing floors, underground activity at West Basset having ceased. It stopped working in 1899. When the engine was scrapped, its bob was moved to Pascoe's shaft for use as an underground balance box for Pascoe's 80-inch engine. Unusually the stack is inside the house. Thomas's shaft reached the 170-fathom (311m) level.

West Basset Stamps (SW689402)

On the lower slopes of Carn Brea just north of Carnkie is the tall engine house and separate stack (both Listed Grade II) of a 40-inch stamps engine built by Tuckingmill Foundry, Camborne, in 1875 to alleviate the mine's previously inadequate stamping capacity. The engine proved to be particularly efficient and drove 80 heads of stamps, 32 on one side of the crankshaft and twin flywheel loading (reinforced with concrete in the 20th century) and 48 on the other. The engine, which was unusual in having cam-driven valve gear on one side of the cylinder, had an auxiliary "back bob" that drew water for dressing purposes from a shallow shaft at the rear. The cylinder opening is consequently in the NE side wall rather than the rear wall. Inside the house, the cylinder bedstones are still in place. The boiler house for the engine's two boilers lay between the engine house and the separate stack to the north.

The stamps engine house stands above one of the finest surviving 19th century dressing floors in Cornwall where the crushed ore was concentrated. Closest to the stamps is the vanner house (Listed

Grade II) built in 1906, which contained shaking tables known as Frue vanners that carried agitated continuous belts used to separate the heavier black tin

Two views of West Basset 40-inch stamps engine house and dressing floors (2010 and 1968).

Two views of the engine houses of Lyle's 80-inch pumping engine (right) and 27-inch whim at Wheal Basset (2010 and 1968).

were used for gravitationally separating the heavy tin ore from the lighter waste. The building in the west corner housed twin Brunton calciners, in which the ore was roasted to drive off the arsenic. The calciner stack (also Listed Grade II) stands to the NW. The ore was brought in along a tramway from Thomas's (and later Marriott's) shaft near Piece, beside which water for the dressing floors was channeled from Thomas's 60-inch engine. Later, a second (inclined) tramway was added from Lyle's shaft immediately south that continued up to Wheal Basset stamps.

8. WHEAL BASSET

Wheal Basset in the village of Carnkie formally came into existence with the granting of a lease in 1851, but the mine had been worked as South Wheal Basset since 1815. Mining activity in the area, however, is much older than this – Carnkie Bal, which occupied the same

from the lighter waste. The tables were driven by a small steam engine housed in the projecting part of the SE wall. The mill building below was built in 1875 and added to in 1892, and contains well-preserved circular convex and concave concrete depressions that mark the sites of former buddles. Like the vanners, these

site, dating to the 16th century. Like other mines in the district, Wheal Basset was an important copper producer in the mid 19th century, with an output of 75,000 tons between 1851 and 1870. Following this, however, copper production dwindled to almost nothing by 1880. But in 1878, the mine took over its defunct neighbour, North Wheal Basset, and from these workings discovered the tin deposits of the Great Flat Lode. In the 1880s, development focused on former North Wheal Basset, around Lyle's shaft, and tin production steadily rose. In 1896, the mine merged with West Wheal Basset and South Wheal Frances to form Basset Mines Ltd, which continued until 1918 when a slump in tin prices forced it to close. From 1885 to 1913 the mine produced over 15,000 tons of black tin. It was said that the pumping engine's boilers burnt 10 tons of coal for every ton of tin raised.

Lyle's pumping engine and whim (SW688401)

Within the village of Carnkie stand the engine houses of Lyle's pumping engine and whim (both Listed Grade II). Lyle's 80-inch pumping engine was built by Harvey of Co. of Hayle to the design of John Hocking and erected on Lyle's shaft in 1879. It was the third engine to have occupied this site, which belonged to North Wheal Basset until it closed in 1872. The engine also pumped from Grace's shaft, 150 metres to the west, by way of flat rods. Unusually, the engine house had boiler houses on both sides, the larger one to the west (the roofline of which can be seen on the engine house) also supplying the adjacent whim. The walls of the second (eastern) boiler house

are visible on the east side. The whim house contained a 27-inch winding engine erected in 1880 to draw from Lyle's shaft. In the 1890s, however, this function was taken over by a twin 24-inch horizontal engine erected in 1890 at Miner's shaft to the east, the house of which can still be seen (at SW689402). The beam whim was then used to hoist from Grace's shaft until being relegated to handling equipment in Lyle's shaft using an auxiliary drum geared from the crankshaft, the mountings for which are still visible. Lyle's shaft reached a depth of 230 fathoms (421m). The diminutive engine house just east of Lyle's shaft contained a small engine used to re-circulate water to the dressing floors. It is also believed to have driven a rock crusher. The lone stack nearby is of uncertain function.

Basset stamps (SW690398)

High on the hill slope SE of Carnkie is the engine house and separate stack (both Listed Grade II) of Wheal Basset stamps. The house was erected in 1868, as evidenced by a date stone on the bob wall,

The twin 30-inch cylinder engine house and separate stack of Basset stamps in 1968.

The twin 30-inch cylinder engine house of Basset stamps with the rear wall of the vanner house in the foreground (2010).

and is unusual in that it contained two separate 30-inch rotative engines built side by side. In driving the stamps, the two engines effectively combined to form a single, double cylinder engine with cranks on the two flywheels arranged at right angles for both power and ease of starting. The engine initially drove 48 heads of stamps, but by 1895, this number had increased to 96 heads arranged in a line on either side of the house. The boiler house (for two and later three boilers) is gone but lay behind the house on the west side and was served by the stack to the south. Beside the stack is the base of a 12-inch steam hoist that worked the inclined tramway up from Lyle's shaft. Below the stamps is a well-preserved vanner house (Listed Grade II) built in 1908, which contained shaking tables known as Frue vanners that carried agitated continuous belts used to separate heavier black tin particles from lighter waste in the crushed ore. Both the engine house and vanner house were modified in 1938 when dressing equipment was erected to rework the waste tips. East of the vanner house is the house and stack (Listed Grade II) of a Brunton calciner dating from 1897, in which the ore was roasted to drive off arsenic.

Two views of the bob wall of the 40-inch engine house at Copper Hill Mine. The engine houses in the background (left) are those of Wheal Uny (1968 and 2010).

9. COPPER HILL (SW698404)

In the private garden of Copper Hill House (formerly the mine's count house and Listed Grade II) stands the bob wall and base of a 40-inch pumping engine house, the plug door of which is elaborately arched in dressed granite. The base of the stack can be seen in the NW corner. Formerly part of Wheal Buller (one of Cornwall's greatest copper mines), Copper Hill became a separate mine in 1847 and produced moderate quantities of copper in the 1850s and 60s. But it never achieved the success of its famous neighbour and closed in 1871. It was unsuccessfully reopened for tin as Basset and Buller Consols in 1881-85.

The engine houses of Hind's 70-inch pumping engine (background) and 26-inch whim (with the wall of its boiler house) at Wheal Uny (1968).

10. WHEAL UNY (SW695408)

Standing conspicuously on the summit of the hill above Church Combe are the houses (both Listed Grade II) of the 70-inch pumping engine erected on Hind's shaft in 1869-70, and that of a 26-inch winding engine (SW698407) erected to draw from the same shaft in 1880. The pumping engine had previously worked on two other mines, having been built by St. Austell Foundry in 1853 for Great Hewas tin mine, near St. Austell, and later re-erected at Tywarnhayle Mine, near St. Agnes, in 1861. It was set to work at Wheal Uny in 1873. The loading for the balance box lies north of the covered shaft. The house of the engine's three boilers lay on its south side, whereas that of the whim (a wall of which still stands) lay to the west and held a single boiler.

The loadings for the whim's flywheel and winding drum stands in front of the engine house. The mine is known to have been active in 1800 and was a significant copper producer until the 1860s, after which output switched to tin from the northern end of the Great Flat Lode. But the mine was constantly plagued by water. Output fell significantly in the mid-1880s and the mine closed in 1893.

Between 1826 and 1893, the mine produced over 2,800 tons of copper ore and 7,660 tons of black tin. Hind's shaft reached the 244-fathom (446m) level.

11. PENNANCE CONSOLS (SW713406)

Overlooking the B3303 on the southern slopes of Carn Marth above Lanner is the prominent consolidated engine house (Listed Grade II) of a 50-inch pumping

The engine houses of Hind's 26-inch whim (left) and 70-inch pumping engine at Wheal Uny (2010).

engine erected on Baronet's Engine shaft in 1866. The house of the engine's single boiler has gone but lay on the north side. Pennance Mine (which was known as Wheal Amelia before 1860) was a small copper producer. It is known to have been active in the 1830s and 1850s, but production records show less than 600 tons of copper ore was raised between 1861 and 1873. The mine closed in 1874 but was briefly reworked under the name East Buller in 1880-81. The engine is said to have been sent to Spain.

Two views of the 50-inch pumping engine house at Pennance Consols (1968 and 2010).

12. TRESAVEAN MINE (SW719395)

Near Tresavean, SE of Lanner, the modified house of a 32-inch stamps engine erected in 1882 to drive 48 heads of stamps is all that now stands on the site of what was once one of Cornwall's leading copper mines. Lying beside the A393, Tresavean comprised a collection of

Modified house of the 32-inch stamps engine at Tresavean Mine (2010).

older mines, the history of which date to the 17th century. Tresavean itself was active by the 1750s, and during its most productive period (1820-50), raised over 233,000 tons of copper ore (second only to Dolcoath). But with falling production and slumping copper prices, the mine was offered for sale in 1858 and, despite numerous attempts, was never successfully reworked. It was restarted as Tresavean and Tretharrup in 1860 and produced small amounts copper and tin until 1872, and it was reopened and completely re-equipped as Tresavean Mining Co. in 1881-86, but no copper and only minor amounts of tin were sold. During its final reworking as Tresavean Mines Ltd in 1907-28, it achieved a depth (again second only to Dolcoath) of 443 fathoms (811m), but tin production (about 4,000 tons) failed to meet expectations. During this last working, the stamps engine house was modified for electrical equipment.

The engine houses of Magor's 70-inch pumping engine (left) and Trefusis 20-inch whim/stamps engine (right) at Wheal Unity Wood.

CHAPTER 9 Scorrier – St. Day Mining District

The Scorrier-St. Day mining district runs SE from the northern outskirts of Redruth to Bissoe and the Carnon Valley and was famously rich. Although it produced some tin (alluvial tin working on the Carnon River dating from prehistoric times), the district lies within Devonian slates some distance north-east of the Carnmenellis granite and is famous for its hugely rich copper deposits. Among the district's many mines were some of Cornwall's most important copper producers and St. Day, which lies at its heart, became widely recognized as the centre of the world copper industry. During its heyday in the late 18th and early 19th centuries, this was the richest mining district in Cornwall and its mines raised some one and a half million tons of copper ore. To facilitate their drainage, many of the mines were linked by a vast system of interconnected adits, known as Great County Adit, which still discharges into Carnon River below Twelveheads. This remarkable feat of engineering was started in 1748 by John Williams at Poldice Mine, but by 1778, it had been extended past Wheal Busy to Wheal Peevor on the outskirts of Redruth. Ten years later it had reached Consolidated and United Mines and, by 1792, it had been extended as far as Wheal Uny in the Troon-Carnkie district. All told, the system was nearly 40 miles long, drained more than 60 mines, and discharged over 14.5 million gallons a day into the Carnon

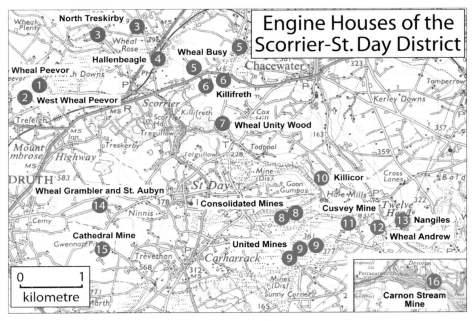

River. To link the district to the sea, Cornwall's first railway – a horse-drawn mineral tramway known as the Portreath Plateway – was built from Poldice to the harbour at Portreath on the north coast between 1809 and 1819. This was followed in 1824 by the Redruth and Chasewater Railway, which linked the district to the new port of Devoran on the south coast. Today, the former course of these two railway lines forms a much-used coast-to-coast cycle path. The impact of all this mining activity on the landscape is dramatic (most notably in the district's richest area on United Downs) and among the many surface remains, the district preserves some of the oldest engine houses in Cornwall as well as some of its most recent mining activity.

Wheal Peevor's archetypal grouping of engine houses for stamping (left), pumping (centre) and winding (right) (2010).

1. WHEAL PEEVOR

Seen from the nearby A30 north of Redruth, the picturesque group of three engine houses at Wheal Peevor (all Listed Grade II) form a prominent landmark, and their arrangement – one house for pumping, one for winding and one for stamping – is typical of a small Cornish mine. Although the mine was worked for copper as part of Great North Downs (its neighbour to the east) at the end of the 18th century, the engine houses date from

its reopening following the discovery of tin in George's shaft by the adventurers at Little North Downs Mine (then in decline) to the north in 1870. As a result of the discovery, Little North Downs was abandoned and, in 1872, the mine's pumping engine and whim were moved (along with their houses) to George's shaft, where the houses now stand. Previously, the pumping engine had been used to drain George's shaft by way of flat rods. Wheal Peevor subsequently became

George's (Sir Frederick's) 70-inch pumping engine house and 22-inch whim at Wheal Peevor as they appeared in 1967.

a small but wealthy tin mine, producing some 3,200 tons of black tin from unusually rich ore. The mine was abandoned in 1887, but its engines remained in place until scrapped in 1900. The mine was unsuccessfully reworked for tungsten in 1912-18 (at which time the three engine houses were significantly modified) and again in 1938.

George's (Sir Frederick's) Pumping Engine (SW708442)

The largest engine house of the Wheal Peevor group is of especial interest in being that of two different pumping engines erected on George's (later Sir Frederick's) shaft in 1872 and 1912. The house, which still bears traces of its original white limewash, was erected in 1872, having been moved (together with the 60-inch pumping engine it housed) from neighbouring Little North Downs Mine. This engine was unusual in having a latticework (rather than a solid) beam and is likely to have been one of two built by Harvey and Co. in 1835 for the unsuccessful de Dunstanville mines in Camborne. Re-erected in 1845 at Garden shaft of Treleigh Consols, which was a near-neighbour of Wheal Peevor to the west, the engine was moved to Little North Downs in 1855. It ceased work at Wheal Peevor in 1887, but was moth-balled on site until scrapped in 1900.

In 1912, an elderly 70-inch pumping engine that had stood idle for many years at Violet Seton or Wheal Johnny, west of Camborne, was squeezed into the same engine house. This engine (like Robinson's 80-inch engine preserved at South Crofty Mine) was built to the design of Sam Grose who favoured placement of the

steam valve behind the cylinder. As a result, the boiler-side (east) wall of the engine house has openings for two steam inlets, one just above and behind the boiler house door for the 60-inch engine and another at the rear for the 70-inch (the lower opening with a wooden lintel is the drain for the cylinder's steam jacket). One brick arch of the boiler house (which held two boilers) still survives, as does the diagonal flue to the base of the stack on the opposite side of the engine house. The granite loadings (modified with concrete for use in 1912) set at right angles to the house on the east side of the open shaft (now secured with a grating) served the engine's balance box and one side of the condenser cistern. George's (Sir Frederick's) shaft was drained to 48 fathoms (88m) by the Great County Adit and eventually reached a depth of about 170 fathoms (311m).

George's (Sir Frederick's) 70-inch pumping engine house at Wheal Peevor showing loadings for the balance box (left) and surviving arch of boiler house (right). The upper openings in the side wall are the steam inlets for the two engines that occupied the house (2010).

Two views of George's (Sir Frederick's) 22-inch winding engine house at Wheal Peevor, the older view seen through the surviving arch of the boiler house of the pumping engine (2010 and 1967).

George's (Sir Frederick's) Whim (SW708442)

Immediately east of the pumping engine house is the house of a 22-inch winding engine erected to hoist from George's shaft in 1872. Both the engine and house were moved to the site from Little North Downs Mine, the burrow and count house of which stand distantly to the north. The boiler house (for a single boiler) lay alongside to the south. The stone loadings in front of the house are those of the flywheel and drum, but the concrete foundations are those of a twin-cylinder horizontal steam whim installed to hoist from the shaft (renamed Sir Frederick's) in 1912.

Stamps Engine (SW707442)

West of the main pumping and haulage shaft, the third engine house of the group

Two views of the 32-inch stamps engine house at Wheal Peevor, showing the cylinder opening in the side wall and modifications made in 1912 to accommodate the horizontal gas-oil engine used to drive Californian stamps (2010 and 1967).

is that of a 32-inch engine erected in 1876 to drive a set of Cornish stamps. To avoid obstructing the ore feed to the stamps, the boiler house (for two boilers) was positioned behind the house and the cylinder opening placed in the south side wall. Evidence of the stamps in front of the house has been largely lost to alterations made in 1912, when the house was modified to accommodate a 150 HP horizontal gas-oil engine used to drive 20 heads of Californian stamps and power the dressing floors. The existing footings in front of the house are those of the new stamps, and the tall concrete plinth behind them carried a stone crusher. The square hole alongside the cylinder opening accommodated the engine's drive shaft. Below the stamps are the foundations of three round buddles (used

for concentrating the ore), beyond which were the dressing floors. Also at this time, the plug door of the engine house was enlarged to accommodate the belt drive of

Mitchell's 50-inch pumping engine house at West Peevor Mine (2010).

Mitchell's 50-inch pumping engine house at West Peevor Mine showing the headgear erected during the attempt to reopen the shaft in 1968.

the horizontal engine, and two iron pipes were installed to support the bob wall. West of the dressing floors are the remains of two Brunton calciners (SW706422) built during the mine's heyday when arsenic was a marketable product. The nearby stack that served the calciners is much older and is probably that of an early pumping engine that was later reused to vent the arsenic flue.

2. WEST PEEVOR MINE

West Peevor Mine, situated in the valley immediately below Wheal Peevor, was an unsuccessful spin-off from its rich neighbour. The two engine houses here were erected in 1882, but the mine closed just five years later having produced less than 280 tons of black tin. In 1968, the mine saw renewed activity when, encouraged by the results of drilling, Mitchell's shaft was reopened. But at the 28-fathom (51m) level, the shaft was found to be irreparably blocked and the venture was abandoned. The lorry access road made for this abortive activity cut through part of Wheal Peevor's dressing floors just east of the calciners.

Mitchell's Pumping Engine (SW706440)

The decapitated engine house (Listed Grade II) hidden on the valley floor is that of a 50-inch pumping engine erected at Mitchell's shaft (presumably secondhand) in 1882. The large eduction opening below the plug door points to a recessed condenser cistern, suggesting the engine had a short outdoor stroke. The house of the engine's single boiler lay alongside to the east. The top floor of the house was removed for safety reasons in 1968 when an attempt was made to reopen the now-capped shaft. The elevated concrete platform west of the shaft carried a small electric hoist used at this time. When the mine closed in 1887, Mitchell's shaft was 93 fathoms (170m) deep.

West Peevor Stamps (SW705440)

On the valley side west of Mitchell's shaft stands the prominent house (Listed Grade II) of a 22-inch stamps engine erected (presumably secondhand) in 1882.

Two views of the 22-inch stamps engine house at West Peevor Mine (2010 and 1968). The older view shows in the background the calciners (left) and three engine houses (right) of Wheal Peevor.

In front is the flywheel loading from which the stamps extended eastward. The dressing floors lay on the valley slope below. The engine house, which lies on private land, has not been consolidated and, with its rear and wing walls precariously balanced, is in perilous condition and should not be approached.

3. NORTH TRESKERBY MINE

About half a kilometer NW of Scorrier beside the main Porthtowan road and the lane to Skinner's Bottom, two engine houses mark the site of North Treskerby Mine. Worked under the name of Truan in the 18th and early 19th centuries, the

Two views of Doctor's 80-inch pumping engine house at North Treskerby Mine (2000).

mine was reopened in 1859 and raised over 19,000 tons of rich copper ore (together with a little tin) between 1859 and 1882. There was little production after this date and the mine was wound up in 1885.

Doctors Pumping Engine (SW723451)

Standing prominently on the ridge west of the A30 at Scorrier is the majestic house (Listed Grade II) of the 80-inch pumping engine at Doctor's shaft. This was erected in 1872 to tackle rising water problems, but was only put to work in 1877. The engine had been purchased from the yard of Messrs J.C. Lanyon and Son, an engine-dealer in nearby Scorrier, who

had, in turn, acquired it in 1869 from Wheal Falmouth and Sperries, near Kea, where it had been set to work around 1860. In 1891, several years after it was first offered for sale in 1885, it was sold to Killifreth Mine where it was erected at Hawke's shaft and worked until 1897. The house of the engine's two boilers stood alongside to the south. Loadings for the balance box stand at right angles to the house on the north side of the open shaft, beyond which lie the flywheel loading and base of the winding engine house. Doctor's shaft reached the 36-fathom (69m) level below Great County Adit at 42 fathoms (77m).

North Treskerby Stamps (SW717450)

Beside the Scorrier-Porthtowan road at Wheal Rose stands the two-chambered house (Listed Grade II) of North Treskerby stamps engine now tastefully converted to a dwelling. This was built to house a 32-inch engine that was offered for sale in 1885 without ever being installed. A lean-to wooden extension occupies the site of the boiler house (for two boilers) on the east side, and access to the dwelling has been made through the flywheel loading.

4. HALLENBEAGLE MINE (SW726446)

Standing beside the railway line at Scorrier, two engine houses (a prominent pumping engine house and the remains of a whim, both Listed Grade II) mark the southern part of Hallenbeagle Mine. Between 1835 and 1846, this important copper mine produced more than 30,500 tons of 6% copper ore. The mine was reworked as part Great Wheal Busy United in the early 1860s, but became a separate concern once more in 1864 and produced a further 3,200 tons of 6% copper ore between 1864 and 1867. Following this, it was worked briefly with its neighbour under the name Hallen-beagle and East Downs, but closed in 1870. The mine was dewatered into Great County Adit at a depth of 50 fathoms (91m). In 1943, the mine saw renewed activity when one of its shafts was briefly reopened and prospected for tungsten. The area is presently being redeveloped as a business park and the engine houses have been conserved.

Engine house of North Treskerby 32-inch stamps converted into a dwelling (2010).

Reed's 60-inch pumping engine house at Hallenbeagle Mine (2010).

Two views of the stack and attached walling of the 22-inch winding engine house at Hallenbeagle Mine (2010 and 1967).

The pumping engine house is that of a new 60-inch Harvey and Co. engine erected on Reed's shaft in 1864. Masonry support for the condenser cistern is visible at the base of the bob wall, and the boiler house lay alongside to the east. The engine was sold to Perran Wheal Virgin, near Perranzabuloe, in 1870. Reed's shaft (now filled) reached the 36-fathom (66m) level below adit. Of the nearby house of the winding engine (SW727446), only the chimney (on the NE corner) and some attached walling remains. This house held a 22-inch whim that was erected to wind from Reed's shaft at about the same time as the pumping engine. Following the mine's closure, the whim was moved to Allihies in Ireland where it was erected on the newly reopened Dooneen Mine by the Berehaven Mining Company in 1872. Remains of its engine house at this location also survive.

Iron lintel cast by Perran Foundry over the doorway to the smithy installed for the ill-fated reworking of Wheal Busy in 1872 (1967).

5. WHEAL BUSY

Originally known as Chacewater Mine, Wheal Busy has a rich history of tin, copper and (later) arsenic production that spans three centuries. It was being worked for tin in the mid-17th century as one of a group of small mines and was an important copper producer in the 18th century. In 1768, it was reached by the Great County Adit at a depth of 46 fathoms (84m) and, by 1823, the mine had given its name to the entire group and had reached a depth of 128 fathoms (234m). During the 18th century, the mine was the site of several historic pumping engines. In 1725, Joseph Hornblower senior erected a Newcomen atmospheric engine that was followed by several more, and in 1775, John Smeaton erected his 72-inch "improved" atmos-pheric engine, the largest engine erected in Cornwall in the 18th century. This was followed by the erection of a 30-inch Watt engine, the first to be used on a Cornish mine, in 1778, and a 66-inch Watt-type double-acting pumping engine, the most powerful in Cornwall, in 1811. Wheal Busy was most prosperous as a copper mine between 1815 and 1870 (during which time it raised almost 105,000 tons of copper ore), but following the erection of an 85-inch pumping engine in 1856, tin became important once again with 1,750 tons of ore raised between 1858 and 1867. Around 1860, the mine was renamed Great Wheal Busy United, having taken over several neighbouring mines, inc-luding Boscawen and Hallenbeagle to the north and west. But this was short lived and the large engine was sold off in 1866.

Two views of the 85-inch pumping engine house at Wheal Busy (1968 and 2010).

page 19) at the end of the labyrinth flue from the calciner (SW738445). 750 tons of arsenic were raised before operations finally ceased in 1924, by which time the mine was 140 fathoms (256m) below adit. The mine site is currently being considered for redevelopment.

Engine shaft pumping engine (SW740448)

Beside a small community of miner's cottages stands an historic pumping engine house with a single telescoped separate stack (both Listed Grade II) centred behind the rear wall. This engine house is remarkable in having held three engines. It was erected on Engine shaft in 1856 to house an 85-inch pumping engine built new by Harvey and Co. to the design of James Sims, which worked until 1866, when it was sold. The second engine, a 90-inch pumping engine built new by Perran Foundry, was installed in 1873, but was worked a mere six months before the mine was abandoned. The house of the

A massive but ill-fated expansion of operations in 1872 ended a year later when the mine was abandoned following a collapse in tin prices. Some mining for arsenic was carried out above adit in 1896-1900, and in 1907, the mine was reopened (as Great Wheal Busy) by an Anglo-Belgium company who installed an arsenic works, the solitary stack of which still stands (see

engine's four boilers lay on the east side. The final engine was a much-rebuilt 85-inch pumping engine erected in 1909. This had been built as an 80-inch engine by Perran Foundry in 1852 for a mine near Par, and may have been the one offered for sale in 1862 at East Crinnis and Par Consols. Prior to its move to Wheal Busy, however, it had worked at Pencoed Colliery in South Wales, where, under the direction of Cornishman James Daw, it was fitted with a larger 85-inch cylinder supplied by Harvey and Co. without a steam jacket. At the same time, John Brown of Sheffield manufactured a new beam composed of two, four inch-thick rolled wrought-iron plates. It was re-erected at Wheal Busy in the old house and a new, still surviving, boiler house for three Lancashire boilers was built on the west side. The engine stopped work in 1913, but was restarted in 1923-24 during a short-lived joint venture with Killifreth Mine to the south. Following this the engine was mothballed until scrapped in 1952. During World War II, the engine had been bought by South Crofty Mine as a spare for their large engines, but was found to be of incompatible stroke after the bob breakage that wrecked Cook's Kitchen engine in 1950. It was scrapped shortly after. In 2007, the site became the location of an ecology garden. Engine shaft is 140 fathoms (256m) below adit. The large building (Listed Grade II) opposite the cottages (SW739447) housed the mine's smithy, dry and fitting shop, and carries two cast iron lintels bearing the name Great Wheal Busy Mines and dated 1872. These were made by Perran Foundry for the ill-fated reworking of 1872-73, but the building itself is older.

Black Dog Pumping Engine (SW732444)

Well west of Engine shaft on the north side of the B3298, stands the prominent bob wall of the pumping engine house at Black Dog shaft. The rest of the house was demolished by U.S. troops in the

Two views of the surviving bob wall of Black Dog 76-inch pumping engine house at Wheal Busy (1967 and 2010).

lead-up to D-Day. This engine house was intended for a 76-inch pumping engine that was purchased (possibly from Wheal Clifford, near Twelveheads) for the mine's ill-fated expansion in 1872-73. In the event, however, the engine was never erected, but lay on the ground beside the engine house and was eventually scrapped. The bob wall carries a stone dated 1872, but whether this means the engine house was entirely new or was one that had previously contained a 70-inch engine erected at Black Dog shaft in 1858, is unknown. The latter engine was built by Harvey and Co in 1851 and moved to the northern (Boscawen) part of the mine in 1861. In 1866, it was sold to Wheal Ellen (then Ellen United), near Porth-towan, but was never moved and was for sale again at Boscawen (the mine by then renamed Hallenbeagle and East Downs) in 1870. In 1871, it was re-erected at Blencowe Consols, near St. Stephen, and from there was sold to the Van Mine near Llanidloes in Wales in 1875. Black Dog shaft reached the 50 fathoms (91m) level below adit at 35 fathoms (64m).

6. KILLIFRETH (SW734443)

Killifreth lies south of Wheal Busy on the other side of the B3298, where the tall chimney of the engine house at Hawke's shaft is a prominent landmark. Records of tin working at Killifreth date to the 16th century, but from 1826 to 1860, the mine was producing mostly copper from shallow levels. In 1864, it was restarted as a tin mine and ultimately deepened to 100 fathoms (183m) below Great County Adit at 43 fathoms (79m). A fall in tin prices, coupled with the breakage of the bob of the main pumping engine, forced the mine to close in 1897. The mine was used for a short time by the Truro Mining School before being reopened for arsenic in 1912. Following a suspension of operations during World War I, work was briefly resumed in 1919-20 and again (with Wheal Busy) in 1923-24. A final attempt to reopen the mine in 1927 was a failure and the machinery was broken up for scrap during World War II. Never a large mine, Killfreth raised over 700 tons of 9.5% copper ore between 1858 and 1884, almost 4,000 tons of black tin between 1873 and 1897, and 360 tons of arsenic between 1859 and 1904.

Hawke's Pumping Engine (SW733442)

The pumping engine house at Hawke's (or Richard's) shaft (Listed Grade II) has the tallest surviving stack in Cornwall. It was originally built in 1891 for an 80-inch engine that had previously worked at North Treskerby Mine (at Doctor's shaft) and, before that, at Wheal Falmouth and Sperries, near Kea, where it had been set to work around 1860. The boiler house is likely to have lain along the east side. In 1897, the bob broke and the engine was

Left to right, the calciner, 32-inch stamps engine house and Old Sump 50-inch and Hawke's 85-inch pumping engine houses at Killifreth Mine (1964).

Two views of Hawke's 85-inch pumping engine house at Killifreth Mine (2010 and 1967).

scrapped. In 1913, the house was reused for a secondhand 85-inch engine purchased from Gwern-y-Mynydd lead mine in North Wales after standing idle for 20 years. The engine had been built for Great Fron Fownog mine, also in North Wales, by Perran Foundry in 1872, and had been moved to Gwern-y-Mynydd in 1882. To create sufficient draught for the engine's four boilers, which were placed on the west side of the house so that they could also serve the air compressor and two-cylinder horizontal whim (the concrete foundations of which lie to the west of the shaft), the height of the stack's brickwork was doubled. The top of the bob wall was also corbelled out towards the shaft to accommodate the longer bob. The concrete cylinder bed (with holes for 6

holding down bolts) survives inside the house, which was consolidated by Carrick District Council in 1987-88. A well-preserved balance box pit at right angles to the house lies west of the shaft (now concreted over). The engine was scrapped in 1944. Hawke's shaft reached a depth of about 125 fathoms (229m).

Hawke's Winding Engine (SW735442)

Hidden among trees in the field ENE of Hawke's shaft is the ivy-covered ruins of Hawke's whim engine house, which was largely demolished by U.S. troops prior to D-Day. Only the base of the building and cylinder loading, part of the southern side wall and the flywheel loading survive. The engine was located about half way between Hawke's and Old Sump shafts so

Ruins of the engine house of Hawke's whim (right) at Killifreth Mine with Hawke's 85-inch pumping engine house in the background (1967).

Two views of the 50-inch pumping engine house on Old Sump shaft at Killifreth Mine before and after it was reduced in height for safety reasons. The walling in the background (left) is part of Hawke's whim (1967 and 2008).

that it could be used to wind from both. The boiler house (for two boilers) was to the north and rear, with the stack (unusually for West Cornwall) placed in the centre of the rear wall of the engine house.

Old Sump Pumping Engine (SW736442)

Just west of the road that crosses the B3298 from Wheal Busy is the house (Listed Grade II) of the 50-inch pumping engine on Old Sump (or Engine) shaft. The engine, which came from Wheal Daniel to the east of Wheal Busy, was

Stamps Engine (SW737443)

Immediately east of the road crossing the B3298 from Wheal Busy stands the house (Listed Grade II) of a 32-inch stamps engine erected in 1875. The engine drove sixty four heads of stamps, the crankshaft loading for which (together with two deep slots for the flywheels) survives at the base of the bob wall. The boiler house lay across the back of the building as evidenced by the arched opening for the steam inlet beside and below the rear doorway. Shortly after the mine's closure in 1897, the engine is said to have been re-erected at Gwennap United (formerly United Mines) to the south, where its house still stands. The lone stack to the NE (SW738443), which stands at the end of the labyrinth flue from the calciner, probably dates from about 1890.

Two views of the 32-inch stamps engine house at Killifreth Mine (2008 and 1967). The stacks in the background (right) are those of Old Sump and Hawke's pumping engine houses.

erected in 1875. The 50-inch cylinder was set down into the cylinder loading so as to reduce the height of the house, which was further reduced in height for safety reasons during consolidation at the end of the 1980s. The boiler house (for three boilers) lay on the SW side of the building and the balance box pit is clearly visible at right angles to the house on the west side of the capped shaft.

7. WHEAL UNITY WOOD

About a kilometer south of the B3298, on the road that crosses it from Wheal Busy, a pair of consolidated engine houses (both Listed Grade II) mark the site of Wheal Unity Wood, Killifreth's rich neighbour to the south. The mine's earliest workings were in Unity Wood (formerly Killifreth Woods) to the west, which was well known for tin by the early 16th century. During the 18th century it was also being worked for copper and, following the arrival of Great County Adit at a depth of 40 fathoms (73m) in the 1790s, became a rich copper mine, producing some 30,000 tons of copper ore between 1815 and 1842. In 1843, the mine was 140 fathoms deep, but output had essentially ceased. In 1870, the mine was reopened for tin, but closed in 1880. Following this it was worked as West Poldice (1880-85) and Tolgullow United (1886-1903), and in 1912 an attempt was made to rework part of the mine in conjunction with Killifreth. Altogether, the mine raised some 1800 tons of black tin and 350 tons of arsenic.

Magor's Pumping Engine (SW736442)

The larger of the two engine houses beside the road was built on Magor's shaft in 1872 to house a 70-inch pumping engine offered for sale at Prosper United, near Marazion, in 1869. Here it had been

Two views of Magor's 70-inch pumping engine house (to the right) and Trefusis 20-inch whim/stamps at Wheal Unity Wood (1967 and 2010).

Magor's 70-inch pumping engine house at Wheal Unity Wood (2010).

Three views of the engine house of Trefusis 20-inch multipurpose (whim and stamps) engine at Wheal Unity Wood (2010, 1967 and 2010).

loadings for the balance box survive at 45⁰ to the house on the SW side of the capped shaft, and iron stays used to the support the shear legs still project from the bob wall. A wooden frame survives in the middle chamber window of the rear wall. The engine house was consolidated in 2006. Magor's shaft reached the 100-fathom (183m) level.

Trefusis Whim/Stamps Engine (SW737436)

The smaller engine house (also consolidated in 2006) is that of a 20-inch rotative engine erected in 1872 to wind, not from Magor's shaft, but from Trefusis shaft in the valley below and also to drive 32 heads of stamps. These stood on the NW side of the largely removed crankshaft loading. The engine was one of two 20-inch whims offered for sale at Prosper United, near Marazion, in 1869, and was offered for sale at Unity Wood in

Hocking's engine, having been built new for the mine by Harvey and Co. in 1861. The engine was offered for sale in 1880 and again in 1885. The boiler house stood alongside to the NE. Well-preserved

Davey's 80-inch pumping engine house prior to its destruction (left) and all-enclosed whim at Consolidated Mines (1968).

1880 and again in 1885. The house has two floors and an opening for the steam inlet in the rear wall, the boiler house (for one boiler) lying behind the house in line with the building (see also page 140).

8. (GREAT) CONSOLIDATED MINES

Amid the desolate expanse of United Downs on the southern side of the Carnon Valley, east of St. Day, the ruins of two engine houses and the base of a clock tower are all that survive of this hugely important but very wet copper mine. Although mining in the Carnon Valley dates to the 17th century, Great Consolidated Mines (or "Consols") was started in 1782 as a merger of several interconnected mines, including Wheals Virgin, East and West Virgin, Girl, Maid, Fortune and Cusvey, that had been forced to close in 1779 because of the expense of keeping them dewatered. To remedy this, the merger replaced the seven Newcomen engines used earlier with five Watt engines, and additionally erected

Cornwall's first winding engine in 1784 and an underground pumping engine in 1788. Having closed due to declining copper prices in or about 1811, when the Watt engines were sold off, the mine was restarted in 1819. Two 90-inch pumping engines, built by the Neath Abbey Ironworks in Wales to the design of Arthur Woolf and then the largest and most powerful in the world, were installed in 1820-21, followed by a third (obtained from Wheal Alfred in Gwinear) in 1826. In 1824, the mine was linked to the port at Devoran by the Redruth and Chasewater Railway and, at its height in the 1830s and '40s, was employing more than 3,000 people and had reached a depth of over 300 fathoms (549m). Between 1819 and 1858, the mine produced over 440,000 tons of copper ore, the largest quantity from any single mine in Cornwall. By 1857, output was dwindling and it was amalgamated with neighbouring United Mines to form Clifford Amalgamated Mines. This merger raised a further

The engine house and separate stack of Taylor's 85-inch pumping engine at Consolidated Mines (2010).

105,000 tons of copper ore before closing in 1869, at which time it had 20 engines (eight with cylinders of 70-90 inches), the largest number used on any Cornish mine. From 1899 to 1905, the mine's waste was unsuccessfully reworked for tin by a company called Gwennap United, and during two subsequent periods (1934-41 and 1969-81), parts of Consols were reworked by Mount Wellington Mine.

Taylor's Pumping Engine and Whim (SW746421)

North of the mine's stack-like clock tower (SW 745420) stand the ruined engine house and separate stack (both Listed Grade II) of Taylor's 85-inch pumping engine. The house, which bears similarities with that at Cusvey Mine, is one of the oldest surviving in Cornwall, having been built in 1827 for a 70-inch engine that was recylindered to 85-inches in 1833. The 70-inch engine, in turn, had

Two views of the stack and attached walling of Taylor's all-enclosed 24-inch whim at Consolidated Mine (2010 and 1967).

Davey's all-enclosed whim (left) and now-demolished 80-inch pumping engine house (right) at Consolidated Mines (1968).

been altered from a 40/70-inch Woolf compound engine bought from Wheal Alfred in 1826. Taylor's engine worked until Consols closed in 1869. The engine's boiler house probably stood alongside to the west. A short distance to the SE (SW746420), a stack with some attached walling (Listed Grade II) is all that remains of Taylor's all-enclosed 24-inch whim, which wound from a shaft 40m SE of Taylor's (separate shafts for pumping and winding was normal practice at the time). Both Taylor's and Taylor's whim shafts reached a depth of 230 fathoms (421m) below surface.

Davey's pumping engine and whim (SW748422)

Until its needless destruction in about 1990 as part of a private road widening scheme, the ruins of the historic house of Davey's 80-inch pumping engine, stood below and to the east of Taylors engine house (which it resembled) beside the course of the Redruth and Chasewater Railway. Davey's engine was built by the Copperhouse Foundry of Hayle to the design of Samuel Hocking in 1832 and, on account of its consistently high efficiency (or duty), became the mine's showpiece. Offered for sale in 1862, the engine was to be moved to Wheal Prudence, near Perranporth, where a house had been built to take it. But, in the event, a smaller engine was selected and the subsequent history of Davey's engine is unknown. The house of the engine's three boilers stood alongside to the west. A short distance to the SE (SW748421), part of the house of the all-enclosed whim, which wound from a shaft alongside Davey's, still stands. Davey's and Davey's whim shafts reached eventual depths of 274 fathoms (501m) and 250 fathoms (457m), respectively.

Engine houses (from right to left) of Eldon's 30-inch and Garland's 85-inch pumping engines at United Mines, and the 34-inch stamps of Gwennap United (1968).

9. UNITED MINES

The scant remains of this once great copper mine lie on United Downs immediately south of Consolidated Mines.

Eldon's 30-inch pumping engine house at United Mines (2010).

Originally formed in about 1780 from a merger of three older mines (Ale and Cakes, Wheal Cupboard and Poldory) that lasted until 1805, the mine was reopened in 1811 and expanded to include Wheals Britannia, Clifford, Moor, Squire and Andrew. At about this time, two 63-inch Hornblower engines were erected, the mine being notably wet. In the early 1820s, what was then the richest copper lode in the world was discovered and profits soared. The older engines were replaced in 1824 by a 90-inch, to which two 85-inch engines were added in 1835. To reach the copper smelters in South Wales, the mine's output was taken to the north coast on the Portreath Plateway until the opening of the Redruth and Chasewater Railway in 1824, after which it was shipped south to the port at Devoran. In the 1840s, the mine's output exceeded that of neighbouring Consols and, in 1845, it became only the second mine in Cornwall to install a man engine.

In 1857, United annexed Consols to form Clifford Amalgamated Mines, and an even larger merger, consisting of the Consolidated and United Mines, Ting Tang and Wheals Clifford and Squire, was formed under the same name in 1861. But by this time the mines were falling into decline and the merger closed in 1869. At the time of its closure, the mine had 20 engines, the largest number used on any Cornish mine, and eight of these had cylinder sizes of 70-90 inches. Between 1815 and 1861, United Mines produced some 400,000 tons of copper ore and Clifford Amalgamated raised a further 105,000 tons. The mine reached a depth of 285 fathoms (521m). From 1899 to 1905, the mine's waste piles were reworked under the name of Gwennap United, which produced 500 tons of copper ore, 100 tons of black tin and 150 tons of arsenic in 1901-02. The area's tin prospects were briefly tested in the 1940s, but with no results.

Eldon's Pumping Engine (SW747414)

Beside the main road west of United Downs, stands the modified house of Eldon's (or Little) 30-inch pumping engine (Listed Grade II). This engine was built about 1829 and erected for the sole purpose of pumping cooling water to the surface from an underground stream. It worked until the mine's closure in 1869. At the turn of the 20th century, when reworking of the nearby burrows was started under the name of Gwennap United, the engine house was reduced in height to serve as an office building. The house was stabilized and the surroundings landscaped in 1985. The boiler house probably lay alongside to the south.

Two views of Garland's 85-inch pumping engine house before and after the rear of the building was demolished (1967 and 2010).

Garland's Pumping Engine (SW751416)

Amid the trees south of the road to Wheal Clifford stands the consolidated bob wall of an engine house originally occupied by Garland's 85-inch pumping engine. The newest of the big engines at United Mines, this was erected in 1857 and worked until 1870, after which its fate is unknown. In 1899, however, when reworking of the mine burrows was started by Gwennap United, the house was reoccupied by an 80-inch pumping engine used to raise water for ore

The 34-inch stamps engine house at Gwennap United with Garland's pumping engine house at United Mine in the background (1967).

dressing. This engine was built by Harvey and Co. in 1869 for Batters' shaft at West Chiverton, near Zelah (where its house still stands), and had been in storage at Hayle Foundry since 1882. After Gwennap United ceased working, the engine was moved to Great Condurrow (where its house also stands) and set to work in 1907. The rear of the engine house was demolished for safety reasons when the bob wall was stabilized in the 1980s. The engine's boiler house stood alongside to the north.

Gwennap United Stamps (SW749416)

Standing prominently on the south side of United Downs is the magnificent stamps engine house (Listed Grade II) of Gwennap United Mines. This was built in 1899 (30 years after United Mines had closed) to house a 34-inch stamps engine

for the purpose of reworking the old mine burrows. The engine is said to have been purchased from Killifreth where it drove 64 heads of stamps and where its house (erected in 1875) still stands. However, the cylinder size of the Killifreth engine is given as 32-inches. The house at Gwennap United was conserved in 1983. The massive concrete crankshaft loading with paired slots for the flywheels is well preserved at the base of the bob wall with the stamps aligned on either side. The dressing floors occupied the slope in front. The house of the engine's three boilers lay across the back of the building as evidenced by the square opening for the steam inlet at the base of the rear wall.

10. KILLICOR MINE (SW752427)

On the east side of Poldice Valley opposite Goon Gumpas, stands the consolidated

Two views of the 34-inch stamps engine house at Gwennap United (2010).

The house of the rotative engine at Killicor Mine (2010).

remains of a house of a Watt-type rotative engine that must rank among the oldest in Cornwall. Underground working at the site, which was owned by Lord Falmouth and mined for copper, dates to at least 1734 and records of a steam engine being erected to cope with increasing water date to 1819, by which time the mine had stopped work because of the cost of its operation. The engine drove flat rods down the trench below to a shaft in the valley floor. Although the site is heavily overgrown, the flywheel slot and the pit of the balance box used to counteract the weight of the flat rods survive in front and east of the NE wall. The 24-inch separation of the holes for the holding-down bolts indicates an engine with a cylinder diameter no greater than this. The boiler house, which probably housed round boiler(s), lies on the NW side and the stack is attached to the NW corner of the bob wall.

Shear's 65-inch pumping engine house (top) and all-enclosed whim (bottom) at Cusvey Mine (2010).

11. CUSVEY MINE

High above the Poldice Valley at the eastern end of Consolidated Mines stand the engine houses of Cusvey Mine, the workings of which were first exploited for tin between 1734 and 1764. By the 1790s, however, Cusvey and neighboring Wheal Fortune were important copper producers. Forced to close because of a slump in copper prices, both mines were reopened in 1819 as part of Consolidated Mines, and played an important role in making this great mine the largest copper producer in Cornwall. At the peak of its production, Cusvey Mine was raising over 20,000 tons of copper ore a year. It closed in 1857 and played a gradually diminishing role in the subsequent merger of Consolidated and United Mines to form Clifford Amalgamated, which finally closed in 1870.

Shear's Pumping Engine (SW758420) and Whim (SW757419)

Overlooking the Poldice Valley east of Goon Gumpas, the two consolidated engine houses on Shear's shaft at Cusvey Mine are among the oldest in Cornwall. The larger house, which resembles that of Taylor's 85-inch engine at Consolidated Mines, was built for a 70-inch pumping engine thought to have been erected in 1826. This was replaced a few years later by a 65-inch engine, but the replacement most probably involved just the cylinder. The unusual square openings at the front of the side walls are those of the wooden beam used to anchor the valve gear (a feature of early engines). The boiler house lay alongside to the north. Shear's shaft, which is open but covered with a grating, reached the 150-fathom (274m) level. The smaller house, which was erected first, is that of an all-enclosed whim that hoisted from the same shaft. The separate stack that stands between the two houses served both engines and possibly also the arsenic flue, traces of which can be seen on the hillside below. Both the engine houses and separate stack are Listed Grade II.

12. WHEAL ANDREW (SW761419)

Beside the road south of Twelveheads, where the course of the Redruth and Chasewater Railway crosses the Poldice Valley, is the unusual pumping engine house (cut down to a barn before being converted into a dwelling) of Wheal Andrew (also known as Wheal Friendship). This house is likely to have contained a large inverted engine with its bob underneath the cylinder – an "underbob" arrangement that reduced the height and, hence, the cost of the engine house. If so, the bob would have emerged from what is now a window at the base of the wall facing the road to pump from a shaft immediately in front. The decapitated stack is attached to the west corner of the house, but the site of the boiler house is uncertain. The house to the immediate north was the mine's count house. Wheal Andrew produced almost 1,500 tons of 7.5% copper ore between 1845 and 1848.

13. NANGILES MINE

Southwest of Twelveheads, a large burrow on the north side of the Poldice

The house of the "underbob" pumping engine at Wheal Andrew (2010).

Valley marks the site of Nangiles (or Bread and Cheese) Mine, records of which date to 1822, by which time the mine was already 88 fathoms (161m) deep. In 1847, a 70-inch engine was erected, but this was sold to Crane and Bejawsa Mine in Camborne in 1850 (and then to Pednandrea Mine in Redruth, in 1853, where it worked until 1891). Records for Nangiles show that it sold over 1,500 tons of 6% copper ore between 1863 and 1868, almost 100 tons of black tin for the periods 1855-1876 and 1901-1905, and 300 tons of zinc ore in 1856, 1858 and 1866. In 1905, it was absorbed into Falmouth Consolidated Mines, which closed in 1915. It subsequently became part of Wheal Jane, which was worked for tin in 1969-78 and 1980-91. The mine also produced large quantities of arsenopyrite, which caused the mine water to be extremely acidic. In 1992, after the pumps at Wheal Jane were shut down, the increased water pressure broke the

concrete plug in the Nangiles adit and huge quantities of toxic metal-rich water were released into the Carnon River, contaminating the entire river system and parts of Carrick Roads in Falmouth Bay.

Pumping Engine (SW764420)

At the summit of the prominent burrow at Nangiles stands part of the bob wall of an 80-inch pumping engine erected on Engine shaft in 1862. It was bought by Messrs. J.C. Lanyon and Son of Scorrier and sold to Wheal Rose United, near Scorrier, in 1872 (where it was re-erected by John Hocking), only to be re-bought by Lanyon and Son in 1874 and sold to Holmbush Mine, near Callington, where it remained until 1892. The house and attached stack were demolished in 1967 for safety reasons when the shaft was

Two views of the surviving bob wall of the 80-inch pumping engine house at Nangiles Mine. The lower view shows Engine shaft being refurbished when the mine was reopened as part of Wheal Jane (2010 and 1969).

being examined for reuse by Wheal Jane. Engine shaft, which is open but covered with a concrete slab, reached the 130-fathom (234m) level.

Stamps Engine (SW SW765420)

The largely complete but entirely obscured engine house of the mine's stamps survives in the woods to the east of Engine shaft. This was built for a 36-inch stamps engine bought from the Welsh Gold Mining Co. (to whom it had been supplied new in 1864) and shipped from Aberdovey to Devoran in 1871. The engine drove 84 heads of Cornish stamps to the west of the surviving crankshaft loading, which contains two flywheel pits that match paired slots in the bob wall. Because the house is set into the hillside, the plug door served as the cylinder

Two views of the 36-inch stamps engine house at Nangiles Mine (2010 and 1969). The view above shows the bob wall (left) and the boiler house door and steam inlet in the east side wall.

opening and the engine's single boiler was arranged at right angles to the engine house at the rear of the east wall. There is no sign of the separate stack. In about 1886, the engine was moved to West Condurrow (previously South Tolcarne) Mine on Camborne Beacon. In 1891, it was re-erected at Wheal Grenville New Stamps, near Troon, where its house still stands.

14. GRAMBLER AND ST. AUBYN MINE
(SW717423)

Standing beside the lane to Higher Ninnis, south of the St. Day Road, stands the majestic house (Listed Grade II) of a 60-inch pumping engine at work by 1865 and offered for sale in 1868. The open

Two views of the 60-inch pumping engine house at Grambler and St. Aubyn Mine (2010).

shaft at the foot of the bob wall sits within a long rectangular enclosure. Inside the house, the cylinder loadings have been removed. The boiler house stood alongside to the south. The mine (also known as St. Aubyn United in its last working) was formed in 1834 by the merger of Wheal Grambler (formerly East Wheal Sparnon), which had been worked for copper in 1792-98 and 1805-08, and Wheal St.

Aubyn. It sits over the northern margin of the Carn Marth granite and was worked intermittently for copper and a little tin until its final closure in 1893. As Grambler and St. Aubyn, it raised 8,900 tons of copper ore in 1845-49 and 1855-68, while St. Aubyn United raised a further 1,400 tons (and 300 tons of fluorite) in 1871-81. Powell's shaft, the mine's deepest, was sunk to the 108-fathom (197m) level below adit at 36 fathoms (66m).

15. CATHEDRAL MINE (SW718416)

On private land a short distance south of Gwennap Pit at Busveal, near St. Day, stands the ruins of a 60-inch pumping engine erected on Colonel's shaft in about 1866. The mine (also known as Cathedral Consols and, in its last reworking, New Cathedral) was a small copper producer on the northern edge of the Carn Marth

Two views of the surviving bob wall of the 60-inch pumping engine house at Cathedral Mine (2010 and 1968).

Surviving side wall of the 24-inch pumping engine house at Carnon Stream Mine erected in 1824 on the bank of Restronguet Creek (2012).

granite. Having started under the name Jengenter Mine, it was renamed Cathedral Mine in 1823 and worked until 1842. Around 1866, it was reopened and in 1874-81 raised 585 tons of 7% copper ore. In 1882, it was flooded as a result of holing into older workings and, in 1885, it was abandoned and the engine was offered for sale. Of the house, only the bob wall, cylinder loadings and portions of the side walls survive. The boiler house probably lay alongside to the NE, while the whim engine sat in the overgrown area to the SE. Colonel's shaft was sunk to the 84-fathom (154m) level below the adit depth of 18 fathoms (33m).

16. CARNON STREAM (SW803388)

On the north bank of Restronguet Creek, less than a kilometer east of Devoran, stands the surviving side wall (Listed Grade II) of one of the oldest engine houses in Cornwall. The building marks the site of Carnon Stream Mine, which worked tin gravels beneath the riverbed, and was erected to house a 24-inch pumping engine in 1824. Openings in the wall suggest the boiler house lay beyond it, on ground since removed by erosion. The engine pumped from shafts sunk on artificial islands in mid-estuary by way of flat rods supported on trestles. Levels were also driven out through the gravel bed from a shaft sunk on the shore. Although the alluvial tin fetched high prices on account of its purity, the mine ceased working and the engine was offered for sale in 1830 following complaints from the Redruth and Chacewater Railway Company, which served the port of Devoran, that mining operations were obstructing navigation. The remaining wall was consolidated in 2000 by Feock Parish Council.

Brunton Calciner See calciner.

Buddle Circular pit (4-6m across) with rotating brushes used to concentrate tin ore, usually by feeding an ore slurry to a raised centre (convex buddle) and allowing gravity to carry the light waste to the edges while the heavier ore collected near the middle. In concave buddles, used for finer material, the slurry was fed at the circumference.

Burning House See calciner

Burrow Tip or dump of mined rock waste

Calciner Furnace used to roast ores to drive off impurities such as sulphur and arsenic. The commonly used Brunton calciner had a slowly rotating hearth. After arsenic became a marketable side-product in the late 19th century, the fumes were passed through a long meandering flue (labyrinth), on the brick walls of which the arsenic condensed and could be collected.

Camshaft Axle with projections (cams) used in Cornish stamps to raise and drop timber or iron rods (lifters) as the axle rotated.

Capstan Winding drum with projecting arms for manual operation used to raise and lower pitwork in a shaft. In later years these were often steam operated using two horizontal cylinders and worm gearing to the drum.

Cataracts Oil or water dashpot system used to regulate the timing of a Cornish pumping engine. Usually housed below the valve gear in a cataract chamber (cockpit) visible in many surviving engine houses.

Catchwings Iron or wooden beam mounted across the indoor end of the bob of a Cornish engine and set to hit timber blocks (striking blocks) on the floor of the top chamber in the event that the engine overstroked and the piston threatened to strike the base of the cylinder.

Chamber Individual floor of an engine house. Usually three (top, middle and bottom) with an additional basement chamber (cockpit).

Clack Non-return valve, usually of the flap type, used in Cornish pitwork.

Cockpit Basement chamber of an engine house between the cylinder loading and the bob wall. Housed the cataracts in a Cornish pumping engine. See chamber.

Condenser Cylindrical cast-iron receiver set in a cistern of cold water in which the exhaust steam from a beam engine was condensed in order to create a vacuum beneath the piston. The cistern, which also contained the air and boiler feed pumps, was placed at the foot of the bob wall, usually between two outward projecting walls.

Condenser Pit Stone-walled enclosure at the foot of the bob wall of an engine house that contained the condenser cistern. See condenser.

Connecting (Sweep) Rod Long cast iron shaft connecting the outer end of the bob of a rotative beam engine to the crank. See also crankshaft.

Cornish Boiler Long cylindrical boiler with a single furnace flue running the entire length just below the centre line. Industry standard on Cornish mines until the late 19th century when Lancashire boilers with two such furnace flues became increasingly common.

Cornish Stamps See stamps.

Count House Mine office building (short for account house). Often a substantial building with facilities for shareholder dinners and accommodation. Many now converted to dwellings.

Crankshaft Axle of the flywheel of a rotative beam engine to which the crank was attached. See also connecting (sweep) rod.

Crusher Rotative beam engine used to break up softer ores (such as those of copper and lead) by means of rollers rather than stamps.

Cylinder Opening Large arched doorway, usually in the rear wall, through which the steam cylinder and bob were brought into an engine house. Often served as the main access into the building.

Double-Acting Engine Steam engine in which both the indoor and outdoor strokes of the piston in the cylinder are powered by steam.

Dressing Floors Usually sloped or stepped area where mined ore was processed by stamping and crushing, gravity concentration using buddles and other devices (and later flotation and magnetic separation), and roasting or calcining to drive off impurities.

Dry Building in which miners changed their clothes. Often heated by steam from the engine boilers.

Duty Measure of a beam engine's performance expressed as the weight of water (in pounds) raised one foot with each bushel (94 pounds) of coal burnt.

Eccentric Circular disc fixed to the crankshaft of a steam engine with its centre offset from that of the crankshaft.

Eccentric Rod Rod linking an eccentric on the crankshaft of a rotative engine to the valve gear. Two such rods were common, one for each direction of rotation.

Eduction Pipe Large pipe through which exhaust steam was passed from the cylinder to the condenser.

Eduction Opening Hole in the bob wall beneath the plug door through which the eduction pipe passed to the condenser.

Elvan Local name for a fine-grained granitic rock also known as quartz porphyry.

Engine House Strongly constructed building designed to contain (and in most cases provide the framework for) a beam engine.

Engine Pond Broad, shallow pool used to provide cool water for the condenser of a steam engine and also to supply water to the engine's boiler(s).

Engine Shaft Mine shaft used for pumping.

Equilibrium Valve Valve that connects spaces on either side of the piston so that, when opened, pressures are equalized.

Exhaust Valve Valve that exhausts steam to the condenser.

Fathom Unit used in mining (as in seafaring) to measure depth (1 fathom = 6 feet or 1.83m).

Flat Rods Reciprocating rods used to transfer pumping power from a steam engine (or other prime mover such as a water wheel) to a remote shaft.

Flywheel Large spoked cast-iron wheel with heavy rim used in rotative engines to achieve smooth running.

Flywheel Pit Deep slot in the crankshaft loading of a whim or stamps that accommodated the flywheel(s).

Frue Vanner Device for concentrating tin ore. Essentially a continuous, slow-moving and gently inclined conveyor belt over which an agitated film of water is passed that gradually separates the lighter waste from the heavier ore.

Gangue Worthless material intermixed with valuable ore minerals in a lode.

Gear Work Another term for Valve Gear.

Gig Cage used to hoist men in later mines. See skip.

Girder Hole Sometimes bricked-in opening in the side wall of an engine house beneath the upper chamber and towards the rear that held the main girder.

Governor Throttle valve that manually controls the amount of steam introduced into the cylinder and, hence, the length of the stroke.

Greenstone Local name for altered basaltic rock.

Gunnis Narrow trench produced where a lode has been worked at the surface.

Headgear Tall framework (headframe), usually of timber, erected over a winding shaft to carry the pulley wheels for the winding ropes. May also support ore chutes down which the mined rock could be tipped into trams and/or a stone crusher.

Horizontal Engine Rotative steam engine with horizontal cylinder(s), and horizontal piston and connecting rod(s) linked directly to the crankshaft.

Horse Whim Winding capstan powered by a horse walking around a circular platform. Used to raise ore in small mines. See whim.

Indoor Stroke Beam engine stroke in which the indoor end of the bob and, hence, the piston move down.

Kibble Large, egg-shaped, riveted wrought-iron bucket used to raise ore in the shaft before the advent of guided skips.

Killas Local name for the low-grade slate that surrounds the lodes in many mines and forms the host rock into which the Cornish granites were emplaced.

Kingpost Upright central post on a balance bob (or the bob of a Cornish engine) used to strengthen the bob by supporting straps (bridles) attached to each end.

Labyrinth See calciner

Lancashire Boiler See Cornish boiler.

Launder Wood or iron trough used to carry water.

Leat Artificial watercourse used to supply a mine with water.

Lift Pump assembly with clacks in the shaft, usually comprising a bucket pump at the shaft bottom (sump) and plunger pumps at intervals towards the surface. The bottom lift was usually of the bucket type raising water on the upstroke, the bucket rods being connected by a simple clasp to accommodate the shaft going deeper.

Lintel Horizontal timber beam or stone slab across the top of an opening in a wall.

Loading Masonry platform on which machinery such as a cylinder or crankshaft was mounted.

Lode Mineralized vein or fracture containing metalliferous ore. In Cornwall, these usually run broadly ENE parallel to the grain of the host rock (normal lodes), but may also cut across this grain at a slight angle (caunter lodes) or at roughly right angles (cross-courses).

Main Girder Massive timber beam set across an engine house just below the top chamber and immediately behind the bob. This supported the spring beams and acted as a shock absorber in the event that the engine overstroked.

Man Engine Device powered by a rotative engine occasionally used in deep mines to raise and lower men. It comprised a rod with steps and handholds that the miners stepped onto and off from platforms in the shaft as the rod moved up and down about 12 feet (3.7m).

Outdoor Stroke Beam engine stroke in which the piston moves up and the outdoor end of the bob moves down.

Openwork Quarry-like excavation where ore minerals have been extracted at the surface.

Ore Mineral-rich rock extracted from a metalliferous lode.

Overstroke Said of the indoor stroke of a Cornish engine when the piston moves too far down and threatens to damage the cylinder bottom.

Parallel Motion Three-bar linkage between the bob and piston rod of a beam engine invented by James Watt and designed to keep the piston rod vertical in the cylinder by compensating for the curvilinear motion of the end of the bob.

Piston Rod Cast-iron shaft connecting the piston in the cylinder to the indoor end of the bob (in a beam engine) or the crank (in a horizontal steam engine).

Pitwork General term for the pumps, pump rods and other equipment in an engine shaft.

Pump Rod Massive timber beam extending from the outdoor end of the bob of a pumping engine to the bottom of the shaft. Used to operate the pumps.

Receiver See condenser.

Rising Main Column of cast-iron pipes in an engine shaft up which water was drained from a mine.

Rotative Engine Beam engine in which the reciprocating motion of the bob is converted to rotary motion by way of a connecting (sweep) rod, crank and flywheel. Used for winding and stamping.

Sett The boundary within which a mine could legally extract minerals.

Shears Tall two-legged timber frame (shear legs) carrying a pulley wheel that was erected over an engine shaft for the purpose of pitwork maintenance using a rope from the capstan. See capstan.

Single-Acting Engine Steam engine in which only the indoor stroke of the piston in the cylinder is powered by steam.

Skip Elongated steel container used in later mines to raise ore along wooden runners in the shaft (skipway or skip road) guided by brackets or wheels. Superseded the use of kibbles.

Smelting Process of converting an ore to its metallic form by heating in the presence of a reducing agent such as charcoal or coal.

Spotted Slate Speckled slaty rock found in the baked zone of alteration (aureole) around granite intrusions.

Spring Beams Pair of large timbers level with the upper chamber floor of an engine house and extending on either side of the bob from the rear wall to the end of the bob plats. Used in pumping engines in conjunction with the main girder to prevent overstroking.

Stack Tall chimney used to carry away smoke from a boiler house or fumes from a calciner (arsenic stack).

Stamps In the context of this book, a rotative beam engine (usually with two flywheels) used to drive batteries of Cornish stamps by turning a long camshaft (on one or either side of the crankshaft loading) that lifted and dropped vertical iron-shod timbers or rods (lifters) onto an ore and water mixture, crushing the ore into a sand. Small batteries of Cornish stamps were often driven by a waterwheel. See camshaft.

Steam Inlet Opening in the wall of an engine house through which steam was piped to the cylinder.

Steam Jacket Outer case of the cylinder of a beam engine that was fed with steam to avoid heat loss.

Steam Valve Valve that admits steam to the cylinder.

Stool See trunnion.

Striking Blocks See catchwings.

Sweep Rod See connecting rod.

Tailings Waste sand and slime from the ore dressing process.

Trunnion Axle at or near the centre of a bob that rests on bearings mounted on blocks (stools), enabling the bob to pivot.

Valve Gear (or Gear Work) Mechanism used to operate the steam, exhaust and equilibrium valves of a Cornish engine.

Wheal Cornish word for mine. See also bal.

Wheel Pit Deep, stone-lined trough or slot built to house a water wheel.

Whim Rotative beam engine (winding engine) used to hoist ore in a kibble or skip by turning a flywheel and winding drum. See also horse whim.

Winding Engine See whim.

Wing Walls Upper side walls of an engine house.

(opposite) The house of the 30-inch pumping engine erected at Carn Galver Mine, near Morvah, in 1871 seen through the cylinder opening of the 22-inch whim.

INDEX OF MINES

The engine houses of the dramatic Crowns section of Botallack Mine, near Pendeen.